THE
MAP
BOOK

OUTLINE MAPS AND FACT SHEETS FOR STATES, REGIONS, AND COUNTRIES

 Harcourt Brace Jovanovich, Inc.

Holt, Rinehart and Winston, Inc.

Orlando · Austin · San Diego · Chicago · Dallas · Toronto

To the Teacher

The Map Book is a tool to reinforce and extend the geographic knowledge of your students. It consists primarily of two elements: blank maps and fact sheets. In addition, it includes a list of state abbreviations and blank graph paper.

The Map Book can be used in a variety of ways at all grade levels. If your students are learning about locations of major political or geographic regions, have them color in these places on the appropriate blank map. For instance, students might color in your state on a map of the United States, and locate and label your state's capital.

As the students begin to study major cities, landforms, and rivers, they can use the fact sheets as a source of information about these features at the state, regional, national, or world level. Have the students use blank maps to write in capitals or major cities, or to draw and label natural features like mountains and rivers. Some students may want to make special maps showing major rivers of the world, major volcanoes, or the highest mountains.

As you study your own state or region, the students could use blank maps to make their own atlases. They might include one map showing cities, others showing mountains and rivers, and another showing land use or resources.

The blank maps can be invaluable in helping students grasp historical changes. For instance, a sequence of maps could show territorial expansion or movements of people. Blank maps could be used to contrast political features of a region or country in different periods of time.

Another way to use *The Map Book* is to encourage students who are doing independent reports to include maps as part of their reports. A report on the Grand Canyon, for instance, could include the regional map of the Southwest with the location of the Grand Canyon identified. A student reporting on pyramids could identify the sites of the pyramids on a blank map of the Middle East.

The blank graph paper included in *The Map Book* is for student use in making charts and graphs. You may wish to use the graph paper to give the students additional practice when they study chart and graph skills. Students might use the information on the fact sheet to make graphs comparing population or area, for instance.

Printed in the United States of America
ISBN 0-15-372673-3

Contents

ALABAMA

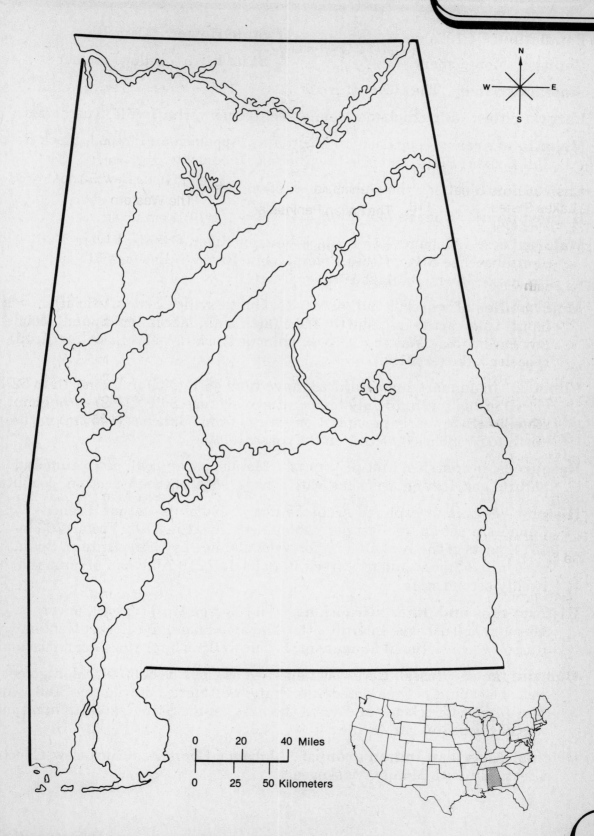

N
W   E
S

0   20   40 Miles

0   25   50 Kilometers

THE MAP BOOK

FACTS ABOUT
ALABAMA

Population: 4,127,000

Capital: Montgomery

State flower: Camellia

State bird: Yellowhammer

State nickname: The Heart of Dixie

Largest cities: Birmingham, Mobile, Montgomery, Huntsville, Tuscaloosa

Major land areas: Appalachian Mountains, Appalachian Plateau, Black Belt, Gulf Coastal Plain, Interior Low Plateau, Piedmont

Lowest point: Along the Gulf of Mexico, sea level

Highest point: Cheaha Mountain, 2,407 feet (734 m)

Major rivers: Alabama River, Black Warrior River, Cahaba River, Chattahoochee River, Coosa River, Mobile River, Tallapoosa River, Tennessee River, Tombigbee River

Major bodies of water: Gulf of Mexico, Guntersville Lake (artificial), Lewis Smith Lake (artificial), Martin Lake (artificial), Mississippi Sound, Mobile Bay, Perdido Bay, Walter F. George Lake (artificial), Weiss Lake (artificial), Wheeler Lake (artificial)

Climate: In January temperatures range from 46°F (8°C) in the north to 52°F (11°C) in the south. In July temperatures average 80°F (27°C) throughout the state. Average yearly precipitation ranges from 53 inches (135 cm) in the north to 65 inches (165 cm) on the coast.

Resources, industries, and products: Metals, paper, coal, petroleum and natural gas, fishing, chickens, cattle, hogs, eggs, soybeans, cotton, peanuts

History: Spaniards explored Alabama in the sixteenth century. French Canadians set up the first permanent settlement in 1702. From 1763 to 1814, parts of the Alabama region were claimed by Great Britain, Spain, the United States, and the Creek Indians. In 1819 Alabama became the twenty-second state.

Historic sites and other attractions: The George Washington Carver Museum at Tuskegee Institute, the Alabama Space and Rocket Center, Russell Cave National Monument, Helen Keller's birthplace near Tuscumbia

Unusual facts: Russell Cave was inhabited as early as 6000 B.C. Montgomery was one capital of the Confederate States of America during the Civil War. The *Jupiter-C* rocket that carried the first United States satellite into space was developed in Huntsville.

Original American Indian groups: Alabama, Cherokee, Chickasaw, Choctaw, Creek, Hitchiti, Mobile, Muskogee

ALASKA

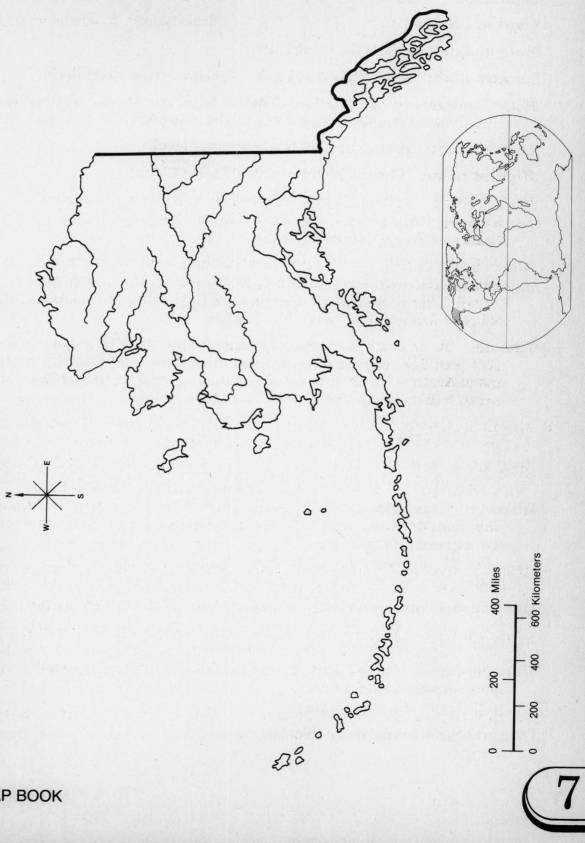

N E S W

400 Miles
600 Kilometers
200
400
200
0
0

FACTS ABOUT
ALASKA

Population: 513,000

State flower: Forget-me-not

Capital: Juneau

State bird: Willow ptarmigan

State nickname: The Last Frontier

Largest cities: Anchorage, Fairbanks, Juneau, Sitka, Ketchikan

Major land areas: Alaska Range, Aleutian Islands, Alexander Archipelago, Arctic Plains, Brooks Range, Central Uplands and Lowlands, Seward Peninsula

Lowest point: Along the Pacific coast, sea level

Highest point: Mount McKinley, 20,320 feet (6,194 m)

Major rivers: Alsek River, Colville River, Copper River, Kobuk River, Koyukuk River, Kuskokwim River, Matanuska River, Noatak River, Stikine River, Susitna River, Taku River, Tanana River, Yukon River

Major bodies of water: Becharof Lake, Bering Strait, Bristol Bay, Chukchi Sea, Cook Inlet, Gulf of Alaska, Iliamna Lake, Kotzebue Sound, Kuskokwim Bay, Norton Sound, Selawik Lake, Teshekpuk Lake

Climate: In the south temperatures average 28°F (−2°C) in January and 55°F (13°C) in July. Average temperatures inland are −9°F (−23°C) in January and 59°F (15°C) in July. In the arctic area, temperatures average −11°F (−24°C) in January and 47°F (8°C) in July. Average yearly precipitation is 20 inches (51 cm) in the south, 13 inches (33 cm) inland, and 4 inches (10 cm) in the arctic area.

Resources, industries, and products: Food processing, lumber products, petroleum and natural gas, tourism, mining, sand, gravel, gold, fishing

History: Vitus Bering, a Danish explorer working for Russia, was the first European in Alaska, in 1741. Russia established settlements and governed the region until 1867, when the United States bought it for $7.2 million. After the discovery of gold in 1896, a gold rush began. Declared a United States territory in 1912, Alaska became the forty-ninth state in 1959.

Historic sites and other attractions: Klondike Gold Rush National Historical Park, Glacier Bay National Park, Sitka National Historical Park, Pribilof Island fur seals, Ketchikan totem poles

Unusual facts: Alaska is the largest state and has the tallest mountain in North America, Mount McKinley. Alaska has the largest salmon-canning industry in the United States.

Original Native American groups: Aleut, Athabaskan, Eskimo, Haida, Tlingit

ARIZONA

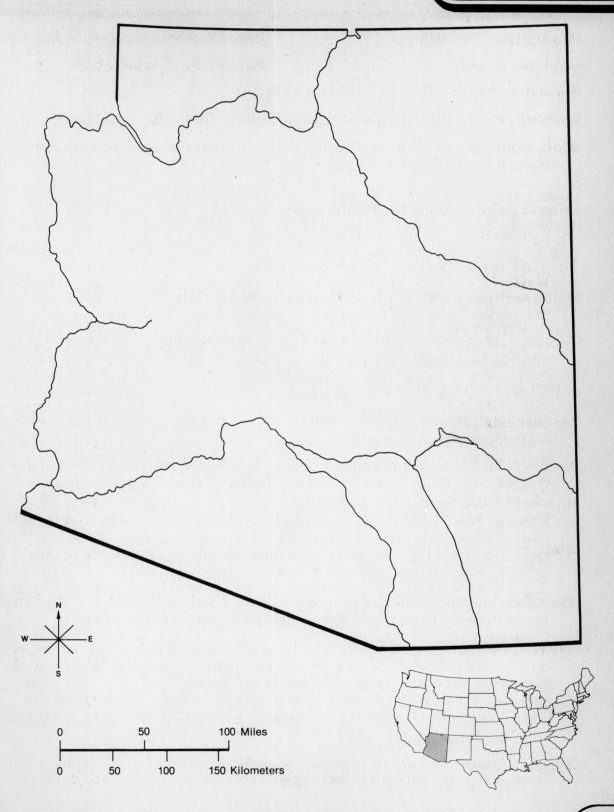

N
W · E
S

0   50   100 Miles

0   50   100   150 Kilometers

FACTS ABOUT
ARIZONA

Population: 3,466,000

State flower: Saguaro (Giant cactus)

Capital: Phoenix

State bird: Cactus wren

State nickname: The Grand Canyon State

Largest cities: Phoenix, Tucson, Mesa, Tempe, Glendale

Major land areas: Basin and Range Region, Colorado Plateau, Grand Canyon, Painted Desert, Sonoran Desert

Lowest Point: In Yuma County, 70 feet (21 m) above sea level

Highest point: Humphreys Peak, 12,633 feet (3,851 m)

Major rivers: Bill Williams River, Colorado River, Gila River, Little Colorado River, Santa Cruz River, San Pedro River

Major bodies of water: Lake Havasu, Lake Mead, Lake Mojave, Lake Powell, San Carlos Lake, Theodore Roosevelt Lake (all artificial)

Climate: Mountain areas often have winter temperatures of 0°F (−18°C). In Phoenix the average temperature in January is 51°F (11°C) and in July, 90°F (32°C). Yearly precipitation ranges from 2 to 5 inches (5 to 13 cm) in the desert to 30 inches (76 cm) in the mountains.

Resources, industries, and products: Machinery, electronic equipment, copper, cattle, cotton, tourism

History: In the sixteenth century, Spanish explorers searched Arizona for treasure. In the seventeenth century, Roman Catholic missions were established. Spain gave the territory to Mexico in 1821. Following the Mexican War in 1848, Mexico gave the United States an area that included most of present-day Arizona. In 1853 the Gadsden Purchase added more territory to Arizona. In 1886 Geronimo surrendered, ending the Apache wars. In 1912 Arizona became the forty-eighth state.

Historic sites and other attractions: Grand Canyon, Painted Desert, Petrified Forest, Meteor Crater, San Xavier del Bac Mission, London Bridge

Unusual facts: Between 1950 and 1970, Arizona's population almost quadrupled because of the development of air conditioning. The Grand Canyon is one of the Seven Wonders of the World. Oraibi, built by Hopi Indians in the twelfth century, is the oldest continuously inhabited settlement in the United States. Arizona has more national monuments than any other state.

Original American Indian groups: Apache, Harasupai, Hopi, Mohave, Navajo, Papago, Pima, Yarapai, Yuma

ARKANSAS

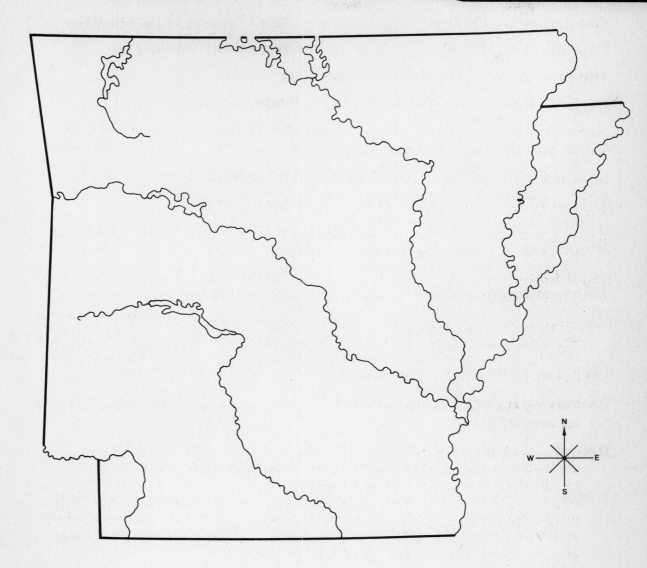

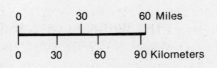

0   30   60 Miles

0   30   60   90 Kilometers

FACTS ABOUT
ARKANSAS

Population: 2,422,000

State flower: Apple blossom

Capital: Little Rock

State bird: Mockingbird

State nickname: The Land of Opportunity

Largest cities: Little Rock, Fort Smith, North Little Rock, Pine Bluff, Fayetteville

Major land areas: Arkansas Valley, Gulf Coastal Plain, Mississippi Alluvial Plain, Ouachita Mountains, Ozark Plateau

Lowest point: Ouachita River, 55 feet (17 m) above sea level

Highest point: Magazine Mountain, 2,753 feet (839 m)

Major rivers: Arkansas River, Mississippi River, Ouachita River, Red River, St. Francis River, White River

Major bodies of water: Beaver Lake, Bull Shoals Lake, Lake Catherine (artificial), Lake Dardanelle (artificial), Greers Ferry Lake, Lake Hamilton (artificial), Lake Ouachita (artificial), McClellan-Kerr Arkansas River Navigation System (artificial), Millwood Lake, Norfork Lake (artificial)

Climate: In January temperatures average 42°F (6°C) throughout the state and in July, 81°F (27°C). Yearly precipitation ranges from about 40 inches (100 cm) in the northwest to about 55 inches (140 cm) in the western and west-central regions.

Resources, industries, and products: Food processing, lumber, tourism, natural gas, bauxite, cattle, chickens, eggs, rice, cotton, soybeans

History: In 1541 Hernando de Soto of Spain explored the territory. In 1673 Joliet and Marquette of France traveled down the Mississippi River as far south as the mouth of the Arkansas River. In 1682 France claimed the region. The United States gained Arkansas in the Louisiana Purchase, in 1803. In 1836 Arkansas became the twenty-fifth state.

Historic sites and other attractions: Hot Springs National Park, Blanchard Springs Caverns, Crater of Diamonds, Mammoth Spring, Pea Ridge National Military Park

Unusual facts: Arkansas has the only major diamond field in the United States. The oldest newspaper west of the Mississippi River is the *Arkansas Gazette,* founded in 1819.

Original American Indian groups: Caddo, Cahinnio, Choctaw, Kaskinampo, Osage, Quapaw

CALIFORNIA

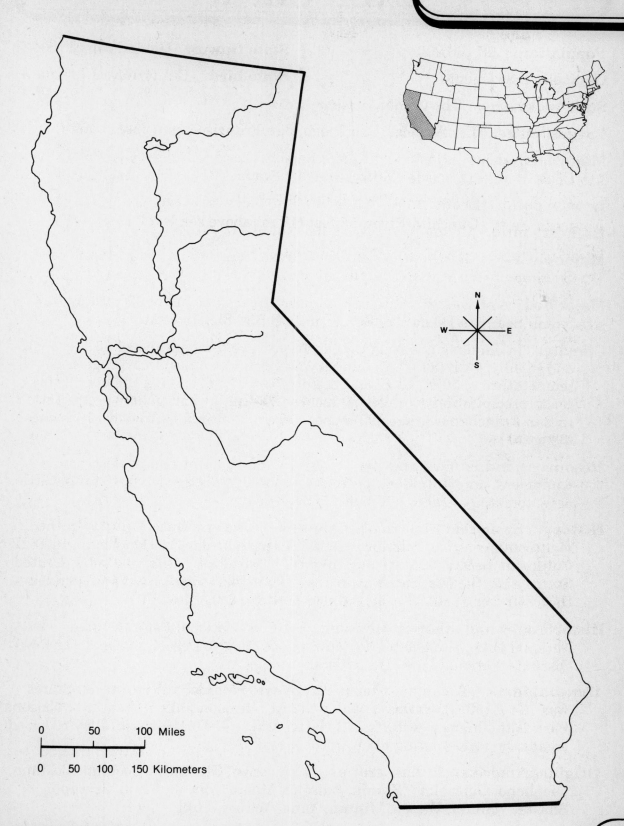

N
W · E
S

| 0 | 50 | 100 Miles |
| 0 | 50 | 100 | 150 Kilometers |

THE MAP BOOK

FACTS ABOUT
CALIFORNIA

Population: 28,168,000

State flower: Golden poppy

Capital: Sacramento

State bird: California valley quail

State nickname: The Golden State

Largest cities: Los Angeles, San Diego, San Francisco, San Jose, Long Beach

Major land areas: Basin and Range Region, Cascade Range, Central Valley, Coast Ranges, Imperial Valley, Sierra Nevada

Lowest point: Death Valley, 282 feet (86 m) below sea level

Highest point: Mount Whitney, 14,494 feet (4,418 m)

Major rivers: Colorado River, Feather River, Mokelumne River, Pit River, Sacramento River, San Joaquin River

Major bodies of water: Gulf of Santa Catalina, Lake Tahoe, Monterey Bay, Salton Sea, San Diego Bay, San Francisco Bay, Shasta Lake

Climate: In January Los Angeles has an average temperature of 55°F (13°C) and in July, 73°F (23°C). In January San Francisco has an average temperature of 50°F (10°C) and in July, 59°F (15°C). Along the northern coast, precipitation averages 80 inches (200 cm) a year. Yearly precipitation in San Francisco averages 22 inches (56 cm) and in Los Angeles, 15 inches (38 cm).

Resources, industries, and products: Aircraft, automobiles, electronic equipment, entertainment, petroleum and natural gas, boron, fishing, cattle, eggs, tomatoes, grapes, nuts, melons, tourism

History: Spain sent explorers to California in the sixteenth century. In the eighteenth century, Spaniards settled in present-day San Francisco. In 1822 California became a Mexican province. Mexico lost California to the United States after the Mexican War in 1848. That year, the discovery of gold led to the 1849 gold rush. In 1850 California became the thirty-first state.

Historic sites and other attractions: Redwood National Park, Sequoia National Park, San Diego Zoo, Muir Woods, Mojave Desert, La Brea Tar Pits, Yosemite National Park, Disneyland

Unusual facts: The highest temperature ever recorded in the United States was 134°F (57°C), in Death Valley in 1913. Ribbon Falls in Yosemite National Park is the highest waterfall in North America. The Howard Libby redwood tree is the tallest living plant in the world.

Original American Indian groups: Achomawi, Chumash, Cochimi, Costano, Diequeno, Gabrielmo, Kamia, Luiseno, Maidu, Miwok, Pomo, Serrano, Shasta, Wailaki, Wappo, Wintun, Yana, Yokuts, Yuki

COLORADO

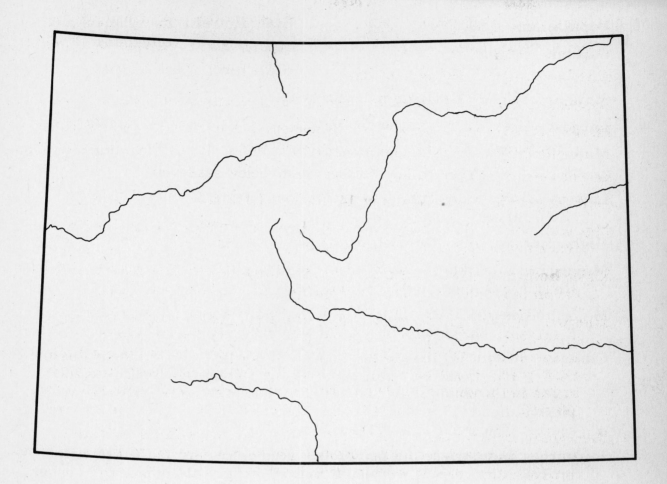

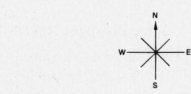

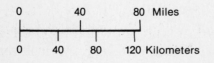

```
0        40        80   Miles

0    40    80   120 Kilometers
```

FACTS ABOUT
COLORADO

Population: 3,290,000

Capital: Denver

State flower: Rocky Mountain columbine

State bird: Lark bunting

State nickname: The Centennial State

Largest cities: Denver, Colorado Springs, Aurora, Lakewood, Pueblo

Major land areas: Colorado Plateau, Great Plains, Rocky Mountains, Wyoming Basin

Lowest point: Along the Arkansas River in Prowers County, 3,350 feet (1,021 m) above sea level

Highest point: Mount Elbert, 14,433 feet (4,399 m)

Major rivers: Arkansas River, Colorado River, North Platte River, Republican River, Rio Grande, South Platte River

Major bodies of water: Blue Mesa Reservoir, Grand Lake, John Martin Reservoir, Lake Granby, Meredith Lake, Nee Reservoirs

Climate: In January the average temperature is 29°F (1°C) in the plains and 18°F (−8°C) in the mountains. In July the average temperature is 66°F (19°C) in the plains and 57°F (14°C) in the mountains. The average yearly precipitation is 17 inches (45 cm) in the mountains and 9 inches (20 cm) in southern Colorado.

Resources, industries, and products: Food processing, fabricated metal products, timber, coal, petroleum, molybdenum, cattle, wheat, corn, sugar beets, peaches, pears, soybeans, tourism

History: Spaniards searched Colorado for gold in the sixteenth century. In 1682 France claimed eastern Colorado. In 1803 the United States bought the eastern and central regions in the Louisiana Purchase. The United States gained the western portion in the Mexican War (1846–1848). In 1858 gold was discovered in present-day Denver. In 1876 Colorado became the thirty-eighth state.

Historic sites and other attractions: Pikes Peak, Rocky Mountain National Park, Mesa Verde National Park, Garden of the Gods, Dinosaur National Monument

Unusual facts: More than one-third of Colorado's land is owned by the federal government. The highest road in the United States climbs to Mount Evans. The world's highest suspension bridge crosses Royal Gorge. Leadville is the highest city in the United States.

Original American Indian groups: Arapaho, Cheyenne, Jicarilla, Navajo, Ute

CONNECTICUT

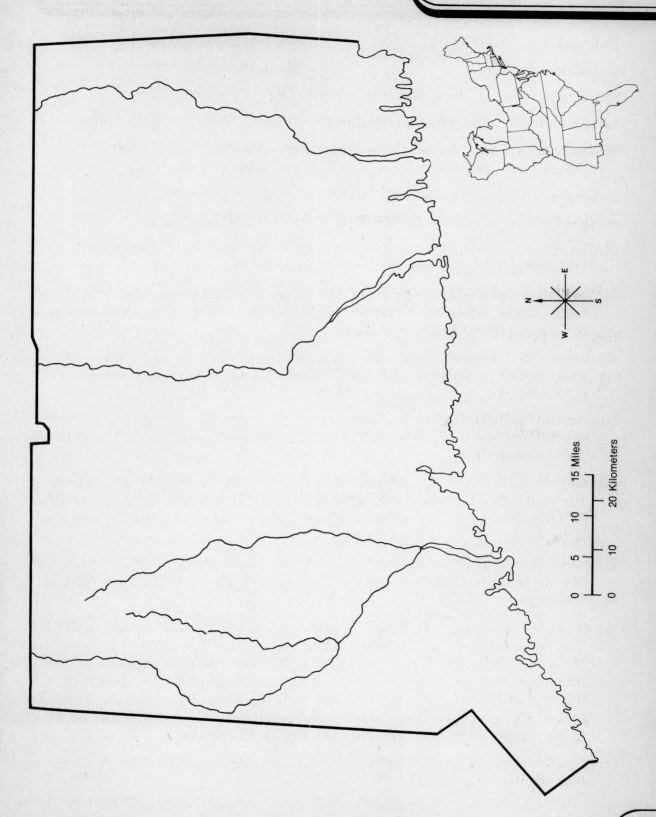

15 Miles

20 Kilometers

FACTS ABOUT
CONNECTICUT

Population: 3,241,000   **State flower:** Mountain laurel

Capital: Hartford   **State bird:** Robin

State nickname: The Constitution State

Largest cities: Bridgeport, Hartford, New Haven, Waterbury, Stamford

Major land areas: Appalachian Mountains, Atlantic Coastal Plain, Connecticut Valley Lowland, New England Upland

Lowest point: Along the Long Island Sound shore, sea level

Highest point: South slope of Mount Frissel, 2,380 feet (725 m)

Major rivers: Connecticut River, Housatonic River, Naugatuck River, Quinebaug River, Shepaug River, Thames River

Major bodies of water: Bantam Lake, Barkhamstead Reservoir, Candlewood Lake (artificial), Long Island Sound, Mansfield Hollow Lake, Pachaug Pond, Shenipsit Lake, Waramaug Lake

Climate: In January the average temperature is 27°F (-3°C). In July the average temperature is 72°F (22°C). Precipitation averages 46 inches (117 cm) a year.

Resources, industries, and products: Helicopters, jet engines, submarines, machinery, hardware, electrical products, traprock, sand, gravel, eggs, milk, apples, tourism

History: In 1614 a Dutch explorer claimed the region. By 1634 people from Plymouth Bay had started English settlements along the Connecticut River. In 1674 the English drove out the Dutch. In 1788 Connecticut became the fifth state.

Historic sites and other attractions: Mark Twain House, Peabody Museum, Mystic Seaport, Branford Trolley Museum, P.T. Barnum Museum, Groton Monument

Unusual facts: America's first law school was founded in Litchfield in 1784. The *Nautilus,* the first nuclear submarine, was built in 1954 at Groton. In the early 1800s, Eli Whitney pioneered the use of interchangeable parts in manufacturing in Hamden. The first American school for the deaf was founded in Hartford in 1817 by Thomas H. Gallaudet. Connecticut earned a second nickname, the Provision State, because it provided so many supplies to Washington's troops during the American Revolution.

Original American Indian groups: Mahican, Mohegan, Niantic, Nitmuc, Pequot, Wappinger

DELAWARE

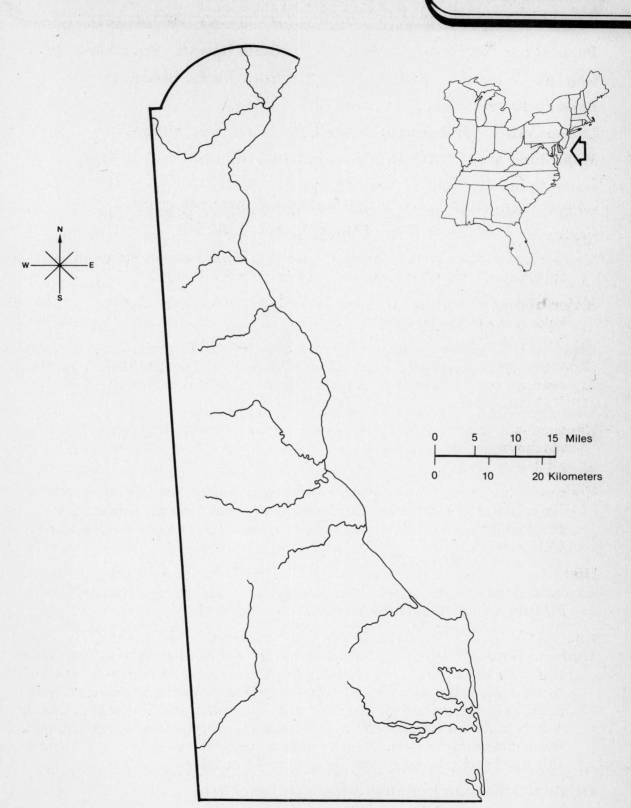

N
W——E
S

| 0 | 5 | 10 | 15 Miles |

| 0 | 10 | 20 Kilometers |

FACTS ABOUT
DELAWARE

Population: 660,000

State flower: Peach blossom

Capital: Dover

State bird: Blue hen chicken

State nickname: The First State

Largest cities: Wilmington, Newark, Dover, Elsmere, Milford

Major land areas: Atlantic Coastal Plain, Piedmont

Lowest point: Along the Atlantic coast, sea level

Highest point: Ebright Road in New Castle County, 442 feet (135 m)

Major rivers: Appoquinimink Creek, Brandywine Creek, Broadkill River, Christina River, Delaware River, Indian River, Mispillion River, Murderkill River, Nanticoke River, St. Jones River, Smyrna River

Major bodies of water: Chesapeake and Delaware Canal, Delaware Bay, Indian River Bay, Rehoboth Bay

Climate: In January temperatures average 36°F (24°C) and in July, 76°F (2°C). The coastal areas are an average of 10°F (6°C) cooler than the inland regions. Average precipitation is 45 inches (114 cm) a year.

Resources, industries, and products: Chemicals, electronic equipment, food products, paper products, rubber and plastic products, tourism, fishing, chickens, soybeans, corn

History: In 1609 Henry Hudson explored Delaware for the Dutch. In 1638 Swedish settlers came to the Delaware region. They established New Sweden, the region's first permanent European settlement. Later, settlers from Finland helped expand the colony northward. In 1664 the English made the Delaware region part of the Pennsylvania Colony. Delaware split away in 1704. In 1787 Delaware became the first state.

Historic sites and other attractions: De Vries Monument, Henry Francis du Pont Winterthur Museum, Old Dutch House, Rehoboth Beach, Hagley Museum Historic Site

Unusual facts: Nylon, first introduced to the public in 1938, was invented in the Du Pont Laboratories in Delaware. Delaware is the second-smallest state in the Union. Delaware is the only state whose counties are divided into areas called "hundreds." Members of New Sweden, the first permanent colony in Delaware, founded in 1638, built the first log cabins in America. Because several large chemical companies are located in or near Wilmington, this city is sometimes called the chemical capital of the world.

Original American Indian groups: Delaware, Nanticoke

FLORIDA

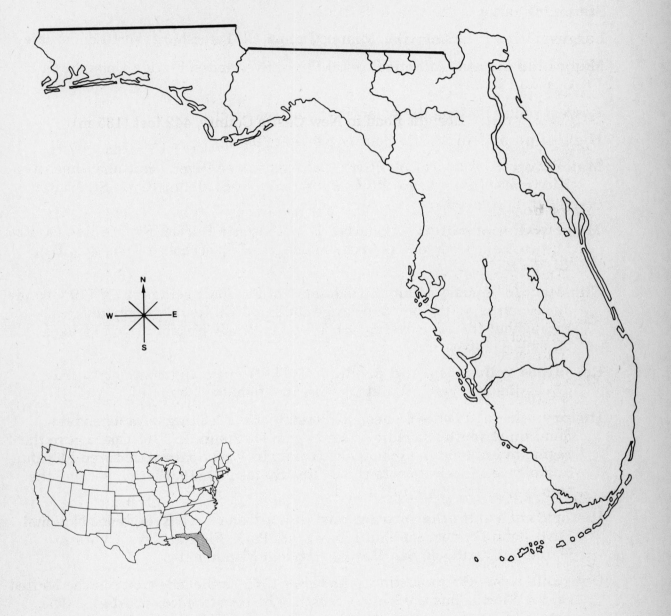

N
W — E
S

0   50   100 Miles

0   50   100   150 Kilometers

FACTS ABOUT FLORIDA

Population: 12,377,000

State flower: Orange blossom

Capital: Tallahassee

State bird: Mockingbird

State nickname: The Sunshine State

Largest cities: Jacksonville, Miami, Tampa, St. Petersburg, Fort Lauderdale

Major land areas: Atlantic Coastal Plain, Everglades, Florida Uplands, Gulf Coastal Plain

Lowest point: Along the Atlantic Ocean, sea level

Highest point: In Walton County, 345 feet (105 m)

Major rivers: Apalachicola River, Caloosahatchee River, Chattahoochee River, Kissimmee River, Peace River, Perdido River, St. Johns River, St. Marys River, Suwanee River

Major bodies of water: Apalachee Bay, Charlotte Harbor, Florida Bay, Gulf of Mexico, Lake George, Lake Kissimmee, Lake Okeechobee, Pensacola Bay, Tampa Bay

Climate: In January Miami, in the south of Florida, averages 67°F (19°C) and Jacksonville, in the north, averages 56°F (13°C). In July temperatures throughout the state average 83°F (28°C). Yearly precipitation averages 53 inches (135 cm).

Resources, industries, and products: Electronic equipment, citrus fruit processing, cattle, fruit, nuts, sugarcane, tomatoes, tourism

History: In 1513 Ponce de León explored Florida, looking for a legendary fountain of youth. He claimed the region for Spain. In 1763 Spain gave the region to England in exchange for Cuba. In 1783 Spain recaptured Florida. Spain gave the territory to the United States in 1819. Florida became the twenty-seventh state in 1845.

Historic sites and other attractions: Cape Canaveral, Everglades National Park, John Pennekamp Coral Reef State Park, Florida Keys, Cypress Gardens, Castillo de San Marcos National Monument

Unusual facts: St. Augustine, founded in 1565, is the oldest city in the United States. Florida has the longest coastline of any state except Alaska. The nation's first earth satellite, *Explorer I,* was launched from Cape Canaveral in 1958. St. Petersburg once had 768 sunny days in a row.

Original American Indian groups: Apalachee, Calusa, Pensacola, Seminole, Timucua, Tunica

GEORGIA

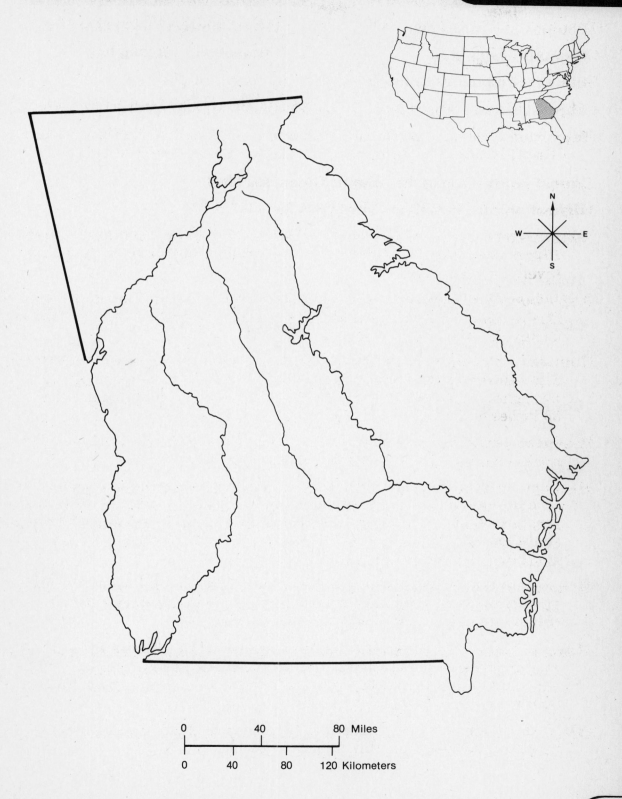

0   40   80 Miles

0   40   80   120 Kilometers

FACTS ABOUT
GEORGIA

Population: 6,401,000

State flower: Cherokee rose

Capital: Atlanta

State bird: Brown thrasher

State nickname: The Peach State or Empire State of the South

Largest cities: Atlanta, Columbus, Savannah, Macon, Albany

Major land areas: Appalachian Mountains, Appalachian Plateau, Atlantic Coastal Plain, Blue Ridge Mountains, Gulf Coastal Plain, Piedmont

Lowest point: Along the Atlantic coast, sea level

Highest point: Brasstown Bald Mountain, 4,784 feet (1,458 m)

Major rivers: Altamaha River, Chattahoochee River, Flint River, Ocmulgee River, Oconee River, St. Mary's River, Savannah River

Major bodies of water: Allatoona Lake, Clark Hill Reservoir, Lake Seminole, Lake Sidney Lanier, Lake Sinclair (all artificial)

Climate: In January the average temperature is 54°F (12°C) in the south of the state and 45°F (7°C) in the north. In July the temperature averages 82°F (28°C) in the south and 78°F (26°C) in the north. Precipitation averages 49 inches (124 cm) a year.

Resources, industries, and products: Textiles, automobile and truck bodies, timber, paper mills, peanut and sugarcane products, chickens, eggs, corn, peaches, cotton, soybeans

History: In 1540 Spaniards explored and claimed Georgia. England then claimed it in 1629, and by 1732 had chartered the Georgia Colony. During the Revolutionary War, Georgia became a major battleground with the capture of Savannah by British troops in 1778. In 1788 Georgia became the fourth state.

Historic sites and other attractions: Little White House in Warm Springs (where Franklin D. Roosevelt died), Okefenokee Swamp, Westville, Fort Frederica, Yamacraw Bluff, Chattanooga National Military Park, Stone Mountain, Dahlonega Gold Museum

Unusual facts: Georgia is the largest state east of the Mississippi. Crawford Long pioneered the use of ether as an anesthetic in Jefferson, in 1842. Savannah was home to the first Girl Scout troop in America, organized in 1912.

Original American Indian groups: Apalachicola, Chiaha, Creek, Guale, Hitchiti, Oconee, Tamathli, Yamasee, Yuchi

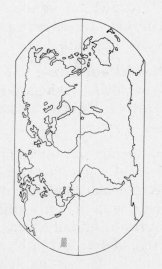

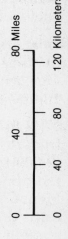

80 Miles

120 Kilometers

80

40

40

40

0

0

FACTS ABOUT
HAWAII

Population: 1,093,000

Capital: Honolulu

State nickname: The Aloha State

State flower: Hibiscus

State bird: Hawaiian goose

Largest cities: Honolulu, Kailua, Kaneohe, Hilo, Waipahu

Major land areas: Hawaii, Kahoolawe, Kauai, Lanai, Maui, Molokai, Niihau, Oahu (all islands of Hawaii)

Lowest point: Along the Pacific Ocean, sea level

Highest point: Mauna Kea on Hawaii, 13,796 feet (4,205 m)

Major rivers: None

Major bodies of water: Hilo Bay, Kaneohe Bay, Kauai Channel, Mamala Bay, Pearl Harbor

Climate: In January the temperature in Hawaii's lowlands averages 71°F (22°C). In July the temperature averages 77°F (25°C). Precipitation varies from 300 inches (760 cm) a year in the mountains to less than 10 inches (25 cm) in the lowlands.

Resources, industries, and products: Stone, clay, and glass products, cattle, tuna, coffee, sugar, sugarcane, pineapples, tourism

History: Captain James Cook reached Hawaii in 1778. In 1795 King Kamehameha I united and ruled most of the islands. During the nineteenth century, sugar and pineapple plantations grew rapidly. In 1893 the Hawaiian monarchy was toppled, and Hawaii became an independent republic one year later. In 1898 the United States annexed the islands. When Japan attacked Pearl Harbor in 1941, the United States entered World War II. In 1959 Hawaii became the fiftieth state.

Historic sites and other attractions: James Cook Monument, Royal Mausoleum, Waimea Canyon, Haleakala National Park, U.S.S. *Arizona* Memorial at Pearl Harbor, Waikiki Beach, Hawaii Volcanoes National Park, Diamond Head

Unusual facts: Mauna Kea is the world's highest island peak when measured from the edge of its true base on the ocean floor, at a height of 32,000 feet (9,600 m) from base to peak. Hawaii is one of three states that have been independent countries. It is the only state with no city or town governments. Mount Waialeale on the island of Kauai is the rainiest spot in the world. (It rains there an average of 460 inches [1,168 cm] per year.) Hawaii is the only state in the nation totally formed by volcanoes.

Original Native American group: Polynesian

IDAHO

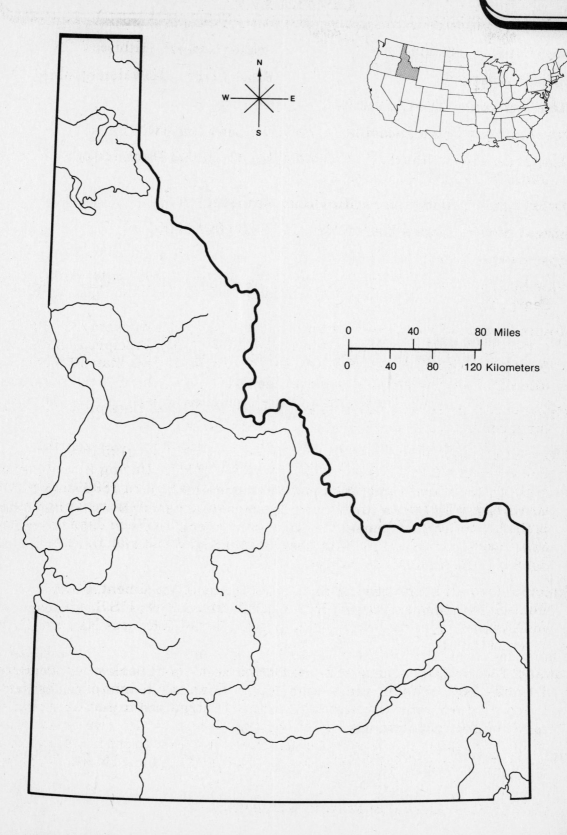

N
W — E
S

0   40   80 Miles
0   40   80   120 Kilometers

THE MAP BOOK

FACTS ABOUT
IDAHO

Population: 999,000

Capital: Boise

State nickname: The Gem State

State flower: Syringa

State bird: Mountain bluebird

Largest cities: Boise, Pocatello, Idaho Falls, Lewiston, Twin Falls

Major land areas: Basin and Range Region, Columbia Plateau, Rocky Mountains

Lowest point: Snake River at Lewiston, 710 feet (216 m) above sea level

Highest point: Borah Peak, 12,662 feet (3,859 m)

Major rivers: Bear River, Big Wood River, Blackfoot River, Boise River, Bruneau River, Clearwater River, Coeur d' Alene River, Kootenai River, Payette River, Pend Oreille River, Salmon River, Snake River, Spokane River, Weiser River

Major bodies of water: American Falls Reservoir, Bear Lake, Coeur d' Alene Lake, Crystal Lake Falls, Pend Oreille Lake, Priest Lake, Shoshone Falls

Climate: In January temperatures average 24°F (−4°C). In July temperatures average 68°F (20°C). The average yearly precipitation is 16 inches (41 cm) throughout the state.

Resources, industries, and products: Food processing, timber, tourism, silver, lead, zinc, cattle, milk, potatoes, sugar beets, hay, barley

History: In 1805 Lewis and Clark passed through Idaho on their way to the Pacific Coast. In 1809 a fur-trading post was established. By 1860 Idaho had its first American settlement. The discovery of gold there in 1862 brought many new settlers. In 1863 Congress established the Idaho Territory. In 1890 Idaho became the forty-third state.

Historic sites and other attractions: Hells Canyon, Craters of the Moon National Monument, Old Fort Hall, Cataldo Mission, Sun Valley, Shoshone Ice Caves

Unusual facts: Idaho has the largest silver mine in the United States. Hells Canyon is the deepest canyon in the United States, with an average depth of 1 mile (1.6 km). Idaho ranks first among the states in potato production. The town of Arco was the first town in the country to be lit by electricity from a nuclear power source.

Original American Indian groups: Bannock, Kalispel, Nez Perce, Northern Shoshoni, Skitswish, Western Shoshoni

ILLINOIS

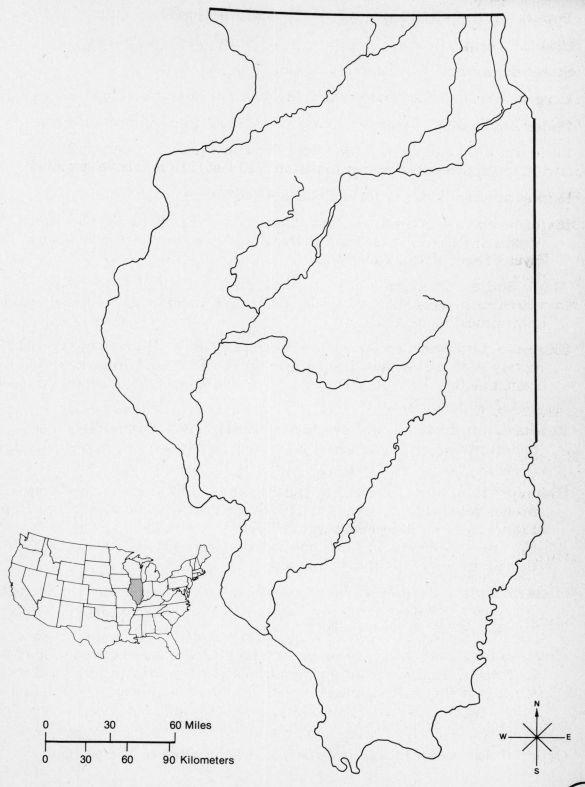

0   30   60 Miles

0   30   60   90 Kilometers

N
W — E
S

FACTS ABOUT
ILLINOIS

Population: 11,544,000

State flower: Native violet

Capital: Springfield

State bird: Cardinal

State nickname: The Land of Lincoln

Largest cities: Chicago, Rockford, Peoria, Springfield, Decatur

Major land areas: Central Plains, Interior Low Plateau, Shawnee Hills

Lowest point: Along the Mississippi River in Alexander County, 279 feet (85 m) above sea level

Highest point: Charles Mound, 1,235 feet (376 m)

Major rivers: Chicago River, Des Plaines River, Fox River, Illinois River, Kaskaskia River, Mississippi River, Ohio River, Rock River, Sangamon River, Spoon River, Wabash River

Major bodies of water: Carlyle Lake (artificial), Crab Orchard Lake (artificial), Lake Michigan, Lake Shelbyville, Rend Lake, Senachwine Lake, Springfield Lake (artificial)

Climate: In the north temperatures average 25°F ($-$4°C) in January and 75°F (24°C) in July. Southern Illinois averages 36°F (2°C) in January and 79°F (26°C) in July. Precipitation is an average of 40 inches (100 cm) in the south and 34 inches (86 cm) in the north.

Resources, industries, and products: Building machinery, farm machinery, metalworking machinery, food processing, hardware, iron and steel, coal mining, hogs, cattle, corn, soybeans, oats

History: Illinois was explored by the French in 1692 and became a part of the French colony of Louisiana in 1717. Great Britain won the territory from France in 1763. It became Virginia Territory in 1778, a part of the Northwest Territory in 1787, and Indiana Territory in 1800. In 1818 Illinois became the twenty-first state.

Historic sites and other attractions: Abraham Lincoln's home in Springfield, Black Hawk Statue in Lowden National Park, Ulysses S. Grant's home, Vandalia Court House, Dickson Mounds

Unusual facts: Prehistoric Indian "Mound Builders" constructed over 10,000 mounds in Illinois, the largest prehistoric earthworks in the United States. Chicago is the nation's largest manufacturing center. Enrico Fermi and other scientists at the University of Chicago set off the first sustained nuclear reaction in 1942. Chicago has the largest post office in the United States.

Original American Indian groups: Illinois, Kickapoo, Miami, Sauk

INDIANA

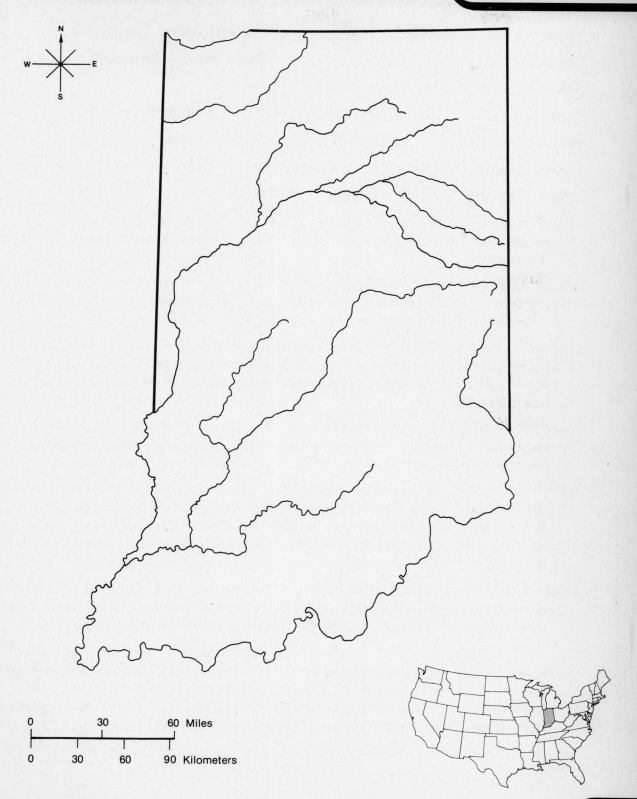

N
W — E
S

0   30   60 Miles

0   30   60   90 Kilometers

THE MAP BOOK

31

FACTS ABOUT
INDIANA

Population: 5,575,000

State flower: Peony

Capital: Indianapolis

State bird: Cardinal

State nickname: The Hoosier State

Largest cities: Indianapolis, Fort Wayne, Gary, Evansville, South Bend

Major land areas: Central Plains, Interior Low Plateau

Lowest point: In Posey County, 320 feet (98 m) above sea level

Highest point: In Wayne County, 1,257 feet (383 m)

Major rivers: Eel River, Kankakee River, Mississinewa River, Ohio River, Salamonie River, Tippecanoe River, Wabash River, White River, Whitewater River

Major bodies of water: Brookville Lake, Geist Reservoir, Lake Michigan, Lake Wawasee, Mississinewa Lake, Monroe Reservoir, Morse Reservoir, Patoka Lake, Salamonie Lake

Climate: In January the average temperature is 27°F (−3°C) in the north and 34°F (1°C) in the south. In July temperatures average 76°F (24°C) throughout the state. The average yearly precipitation ranges from 32 inches (81 cm) to 36 inches (91 cm).

Resources, industries, and products: Steelmaking, electrical and electronic equipment, transportation equipment, chemicals, coal, gypsum, hogs, corn, soybeans, tomatoes

History: French explorers reached Indiana in 1679. In 1731 the French established a permanent settlement. France lost the territory to Great Britain in 1763. During the American Revolution, George Rogers Clark seized the territory from the British. Indiana became the nineteenth state in 1816.

Historic sites and other attractions: Lincoln Boyhood National Memorial, George Rogers Clark National Historical Park, New Harmony, Wyandotte Cave, the town of Santa Claus, Conner Prairie Pioneer Settlement

Unusual facts: Gary, Indiana, has some of the nation's largest steel mills. The longest single-span covered bridge in the country, 207 feet (63 m), crosses Sugar Creek in Turkey Run State Park. The annual 500-mile (800-km) automobile race in Indianapolis (the Indianapolis 500) probably attracts more people than any other single sporting event in the nation.

Original American Indian groups: Chippewa, Miami, Shawnee

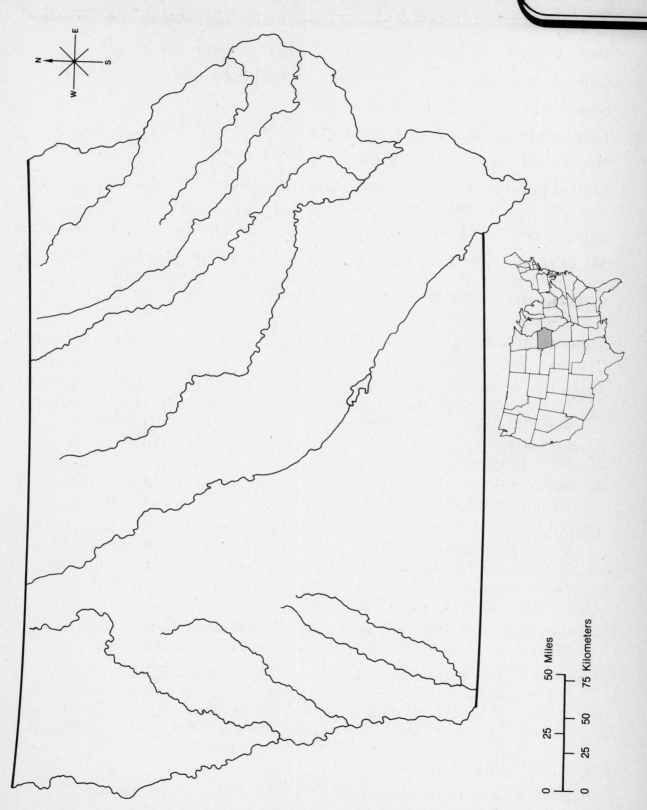

IOWA

50 Miles

75 Kilometers

25

50

25

25

0

0

FACTS ABOUT
IOWA

Population: 2,834,000

Capital: Des Moines

State nickname: The Hawkeye State

Largest cities: Des Moines, Cedar Rapids, Davenport, Sioux City, Waterloo

Major land area: Central Plains

Lowest point: The junction of the Mississippi and Des Moines rivers, 480 feet (146 m) above sea level

Highest point: Along the north boundary of Osceola County, 1,670 feet (509 m)

Major rivers: Big Sioux River, Boyer River, Cedar River, Des Moines River, East Nishnabotna River, Iowa River, Little Sioux River, Maquoketa River, Mississippi River, Missouri River, Turkey River, Wapsipinicon River, West Nishnabotna River

Major bodies of water: Clear Lake, Lake Okoboji, Lake Red Rock, Rathbun Lake, Saylorville Lake, Spirit Lake

Climate: In the north temperatures average 18°F (−8°C) in January and 74°F (23°C) in July. In the south temperatures average 24°F (−4°C) in January and 77°F (25°C) in July. Northern Iowa averages 34 inches (86 cm) of precipitation per year. Southern Iowa averages 40 inches (100 cm) of precipitation per year.

Resources, industries, and products: Farm machinery, food processing, chemicals, hogs, cattle, eggs, corn, soybeans

History: French explorers claimed the Iowa region for France in 1673. In 1762 France gave the area to Spain, which in turn gave the area back to France in 1800. The United States purchased the land as part of the Louisiana Purchase in 1803. Iowa became a United States territory in 1838, and became the twenty-ninth state in 1846.

Historic sites and other attractions: Effigy Mounds National Monument, Herbert Hoover's birthplace, Amana Colonies, Dvorak Memorial

Unusual facts: Iowa is the state with the highest literacy rate (99 percent) in the country. It is the second-largest producer of farm products. Iowa is the leading state in the number of hogs raised for marketing. Along with Illinois, it leads the country in corn production. More corn for popping is raised in Iowa than in any other state. The word *Iowa* means "beautiful word" in the Sioux language.

Original American Indian groups: Eastern Dakota, Iowa, Sautee

State flower: Wild rose

State bird: Eastern goldfinch

KANSAS

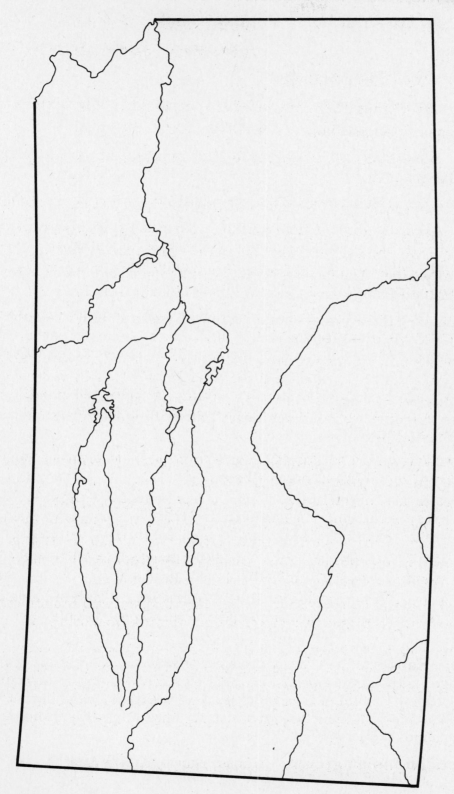

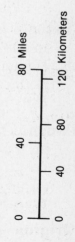

THE MAP BOOK

FACTS ABOUT KANSAS

Population: 2,487,000

Capital: Topeka

State nickname: The Sunflower State

Largest cities: Wichita, Kansas City, Topeka, Overland Park, Lawrence

Major land areas: Central Plains, Great Plains, Ozark Plateau

Lowest point: Along the Verdigris River in Montgomery County, 680 feet (207 m) above sea level

Highest point: Mount Sunflower, 4,039 feet (1,231 m)

Major rivers: Arkansas River, Cimarron River, Kansas River, Missouri River, Republican River, Saline River, Smoky Hill River, Solomon River

Major bodies of water: Cheney Reservoir, John Redmond Reservoir, Kirwin Reservoir, Milford Lake, Perry Lake, Waconda Lake, Wilson Lake

Climate: In January the average temperature in Kansas is 32°F (0°C) and in July, 79°F (26°C). Precipitation averages 40 inches (100 cm) a year in the southeastern part of the state and 17 inches (43 cm) a year in the western regions.

Resources, industries, and products: Light aircraft, railroad freight cars, construction machinery, farm machinery, flour milling, petroleum and natural gas, cattle, hogs, wheat, corn

History: Spanish explorers came to Kansas in the sixteenth century. France then claimed the territory in the late seventeenth century. In 1803 France sold the area to the United States as part of the Louisiana Purchase. The United States gave the land to eastern Indian tribes in 1825, then opened it up for settlers in 1854. In 1861 Kansas became the thirty-fourth state.

Historic sites and other attractions: Dwight D. Eisenhower's boyhood home in Abilene, Fort Leavenworth, Dodge City, John Brown Memorial State Park, Hollenberg Pony Express Station, Fort Riley, Agricultural Hall of Fame in Bonner Springs, Kansas Cosmosphere and Space Discovery Center in Hutchinson

Unusual facts: Kansas is the leading producer of wheat in the nation. "Home on the Range" is the state song of Kansas. Dodge City, Kansas, was once called the Cowboy Capital of the World. It had the largest cattle market in the world at one time. The largest hailstone on record — weighing more than 1 1/2 pounds (700 g) — fell in Kansas.

Original American Indian groups: Kansa, Kiowa, Kiowa Apache

State flower: Sunflower

State bird: Western meadow lark

KENTUCKY

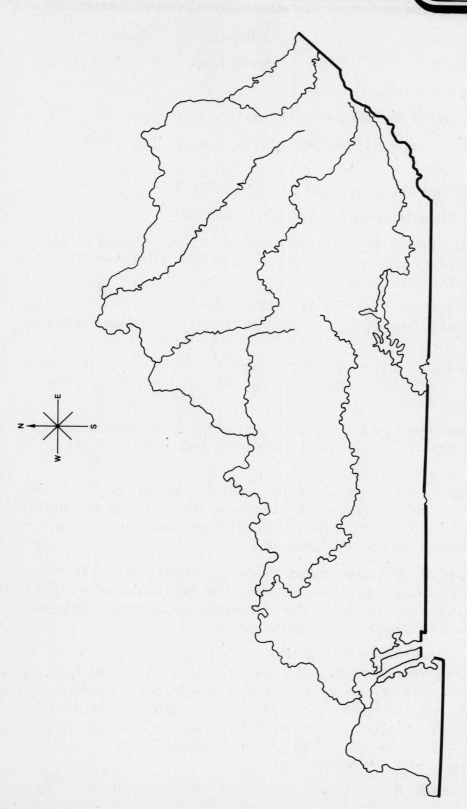

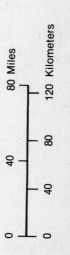

80 Miles

120 Kilometers

80

40

40

0

0

FACTS ABOUT
KENTUCKY

Population: 3,721,000

Capital: Frankfort

State flower: Goldenrod

State bird: Kentucky cardinal

State nickname: The Bluegrass State

Largest cities: Louisville, Lexington, Owensboro, Covington, Bowling Green

Major land areas: Appalachian Plateau, Gulf Coastal Plain, Interior Low Plateau

Lowest point: Along the Mississippi River, 257 feet (78 m) above sea level

Highest point: Black Mountain, 4,145 feet (1,263 m)

Major rivers: Big Sandy River, Cumberland River, Green River, Kentucky River, Licking River, Mississippi River, Ohio River, Salt River, Tennessee River, Tug Fork River

Major bodies of water: Dale Hollow Lake, Dewey Lake, Green River Lake, Herrington Lake, Kentucky Lake, Lake Barkley, Lake Cumberland (all artificial)

Climate: In January the average temperature is 38°F (3°C). In July Kentucky averages 77°F (25°C). Precipitation averages 46 inches (117 cm) a year throughout the state.

Resources, industries, and products: Farm equipment, conveyors, air-pollution equipment, electrical machinery, coal, meat products, corn, soybeans

History: During the seventeenth and eighteenth centuries, the French and English came to Kentucky. The first European settlement was established there in 1774. In 1775 Daniel Boone led other settlers into the area. Kentucky became the fifteenth state in 1792.

Historic sites and other attractions: Mammoth Cave National Park, Abraham Lincoln's birthplace, Cumberland Gap National Historical Park, the Kentucky Derby, John James Audubon Memorial Museum, Natural Bridge, My Old Kentucky Home in Bardstown

Unusual facts: Cumberland Falls is the only place in the world outside of Africa that gets the moonbow, a rainbow formed from the light of the moon. Fort Knox holds the nation's gold reserve. Kentucky leads the states in the production of coal. The Kentucky Derby is the nation's oldest continually run horse race. Kentucky has the world's largest cave system. Kentucky Lake, created by the Kentucky Dam on the Tennessee River, is one of the country's largest artificial lakes.

Original American Indian groups: Cherokee, Chickawa, Shawnee, Yuchi

NAME _____

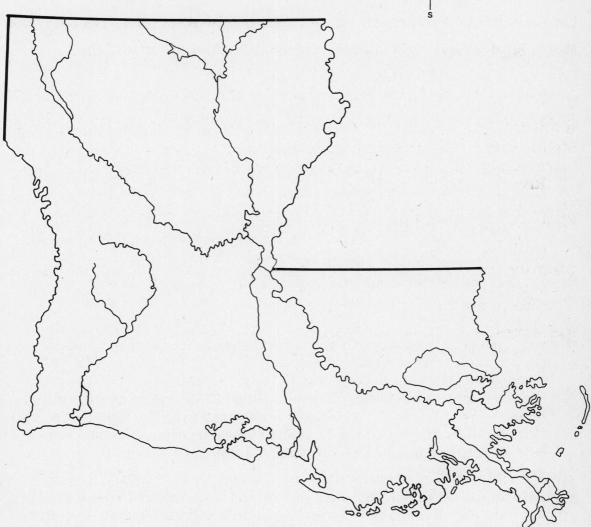

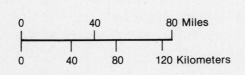

0   40   80 Miles

0   40   80   120 Kilometers

THE MAP BOOK

FACTS ABOUT
LOUISIANA

Population: 4,420,000

State flower: Magnolia

Capital: Baton Rouge

State bird: Eastern brown pelican

State nickname: The Pelican State

Largest cities: New Orleans, Baton Rouge, Shreveport, Metairie, Lafayette

Major land areas: Gulf Coastal Plain, Mississippi Alluvial Plain

Lowest point: In New Orleans, 5 feet (1.5 m) below sea level

Highest point: Driskill Mountain, 535 feet (163 m)

Major rivers: Atchafalaya River, Calcasieu River, Mississippi River, Ouachita River, Pearl River, Red River, Sabine River

Major bodies of water: Bayou d' Arbonne Lake, Calcasieu Lake, Grand Lake, Lake Maurepas, Lake Pontchartrain, Lake Salvador, White Lake

Climate: In January the average temperature in the south is 55°F (13°C) and in the north, 49°F (9°C). In July the average temperature throughout the state is 82°F (28°C). Precipitation averages 56 inches (142 cm) a year.

Resources, industries, and products: Petroleum and coal products, sulphur, chemicals, natural gas, timber, furs, rice, soybeans, sugarcane, sweet potatoes

History: During the sixteenth and seventeenth centuries, both Spanish and French explorers traveled through Louisiana. In 1682 Robert La Salle claimed the Mississippi River valley area for France. In 1699 the royal French colony of Louisiana was founded. In 1762 France transferred the region to Spain. Spain in turn gave it back to France in 1800. In 1803 the United States purchased the Louisiana Territory from France for about $15 million, in the Louisiana Purchase. In 1812 Louisiana became the eighteenth state.

Historic sites and other attractions: Chalmette National Historical Park, Avery Island, Evangeline County, French Quarter in New Orleans, Mardi Gras

Unusual facts: Louisiana ranks second to Texas in mineral production, and leads the nation in the production of hardwoods (oak, gum, hickory, cypress). The world's longest bridge is the Lake Pontchartrain Causeway, which extends 29 miles (47 km). The Superdome in New Orleans is the largest indoor stadium in the world. More goods go in and out of the port of New Orleans than any other port in the country.

Original American Indian groups: Acolapissa, Apalachee, Atalapa, Avoyel, Bayogoula, Chitimacha, Natchitoches, Tunica

MAINE

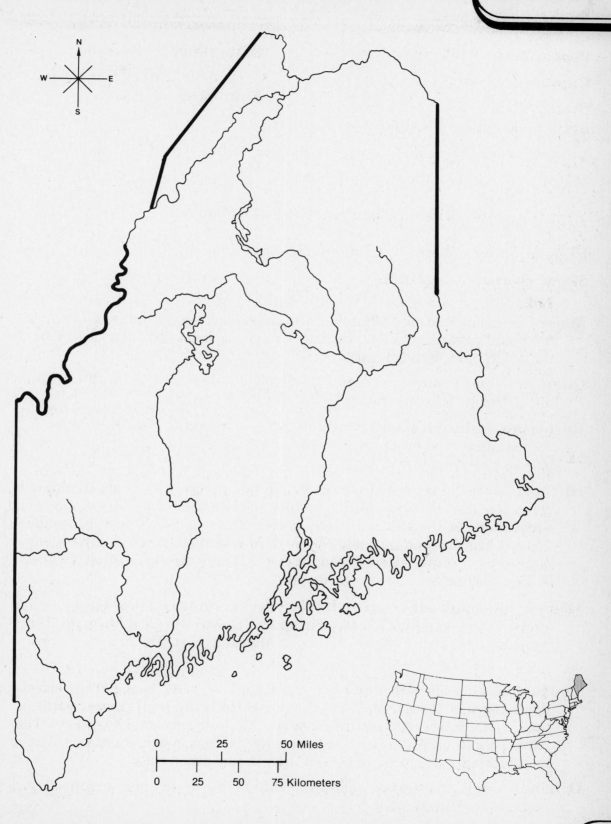

N
W   E
S

0   25   50 Miles

0   25   50   75 Kilometers

41

FACTS ABOUT
MAINE

Population: 1,206,000

Capital: Augusta

State flower: White pine cone and tassel

State bird: Chickadee

State nickname: The Pine Tree State

Largest cities: Portland, Lewiston, Bangor, Auburn, South Portland

Major land areas: Coastal Lowlands, New England Upland, White Mountains

Lowest point: Along the coast, sea level

Highest point: Mount Katahdin, 5,268 feet (1,606 m)

Major rivers: Allagash River, Androscoggin River, Kennebec River, Penobscot River, Saco River, St. Croix River, St. John River

Major bodies of water: Chamberlain Lake, Chesuncook Lake, Eagle Lake (artificial), Flagstaff Lake, Grand Lake, Moosehead Lake, Penobscot Bay, Rangeley Lake, Sebago Lake

Climate: Temperatures average 24°F (−4°C) in January and 67°F (19°C) in July. Precipitation averages 43 inches (180 cm) a year.

Resources, industries, and products: Paper products, leather products, lumber and wood products, food canning and freezing, textiles, lobsters, clams, eggs, potatoes

History: French explorers reached Maine in the sixteenth century. English colonists first settled in Maine in 1607. They established permanent settlements in the 1620s. In 1622 England gave the land to Ferdinando Gorges. His descendants sold Maine to Massachusetts for about $6,000. Hundreds of Maine patriots fought in the American Revolution. In 1820 Maine became the twenty-third state.

Historic sites and other attractions: Acadia National Park, Henry Wadsworth Longfellow House, Burnham Tavern, Old Gaol Museum, Fort Popham Memorial, Penobscot Marine Museum, Fort Western, Seashore Trolley Museum, Sugarloaf ski area

Unusual facts: The Portland Head Light, built in 1791, is one of the oldest lighthouses in the nation. West Quoddy Head is the easternmost point in the United States. Almost nine tenths of Maine is covered by forests. The 2,000 islands off Maine's coast are really the tops of old mountains. More toothpicks are produced in Maine than in any other state.

Original American Indian groups: Abnaki, Malecite, Passamaquoddy, Pennacook, Penobscot

MARYLAND

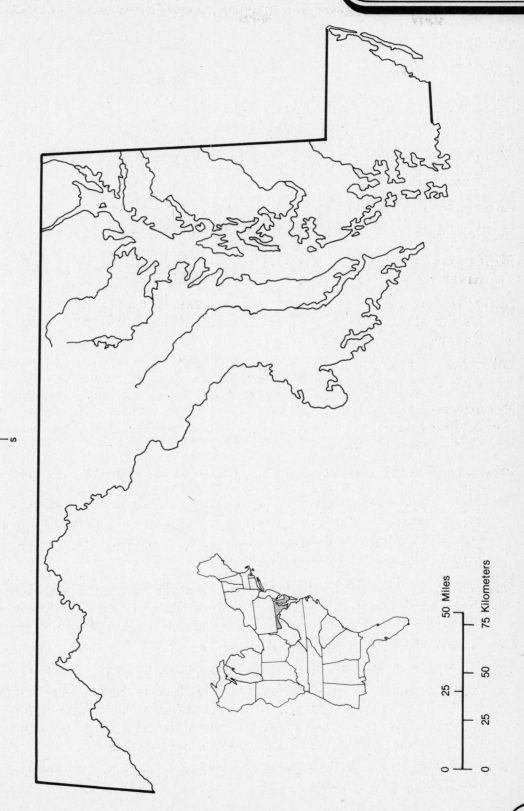

50 Miles

75 Kilometers

THE MAP BOOK

FACTS ABOUT
MARYLAND

Population: 4,644,000

Capital: Annapolis

State flower: Black-eyed Susan

State bird: Baltimore oriole

State nickname: The Old Line State

Largest cities: Baltimore, Silver Spring, Dundalk, Bethesda, Towson

Major land areas: Appalachian Mountains, Appalachian Plateau, Atlantic Coastal Plain, Blue Ridge Mountains, Piedmont

Lowest point: Along the ocean, sea level

Highest point: Backbone Mountain, 3,360 feet (1,024 m)

Major rivers: Chester River, Choptank River, Elk River, Gunpowder River, Nanticoke River, Patapsco River, Patuxent River, Pocomoke River, Potomac River, Sassafras River, Susquehanna River, Wicomico River

Major bodies of water: Chesapeake Bay, Deep Creek Lake (artificial), Liberty Lake (artificial)

Climate: In January temperatures average 29°F (−2°C) in the northwest and 39°F (4°C) on the coast. In July temperatures average 68°F (20°C) in the northwest and 75°F (24°C) on the coast. Precipitation averages 44 inches (112 cm) a year.

Resources, industries, and products: Food products, electronic equipment, electrical machinery, tourism, aluminum, copper, steel, coal, stone, chickens, oysters, milk, corn, soybeans

History: In 1608 Captain John Smith explored Chesapeake Bay. The first English settlers arrived in 1634. In 1649 Maryland passed a religious toleration act giving equal rights to all Christians. In 1776 Maryland declared its independence. In 1788 Maryland became the seventh state.

Historic sites and other attractions: Antietam National Battlefield Site, Fort McHenry National Monument, United States Naval Academy, Peale Museum, Clara Barton National Historic Site, Edgar Allen Poe house

Unusual facts: After the British bombardment of Fort McHenry in 1814, Francis Scott Key wrote "The Star-Spangled Banner." The first telegraph line in the nation was opened in 1844. The state capitol in Annapolis is the oldest statehouse still in use. The first American coal-burning steam locomotive was tested in Maryland in 1840. Maryland is the leading producer of oysters in the United States.

Original American Indian groups: Conoy, Delaware, Nantocoke, Powhatan, Shawnee, Susquehanna

MASSACHUSETTS

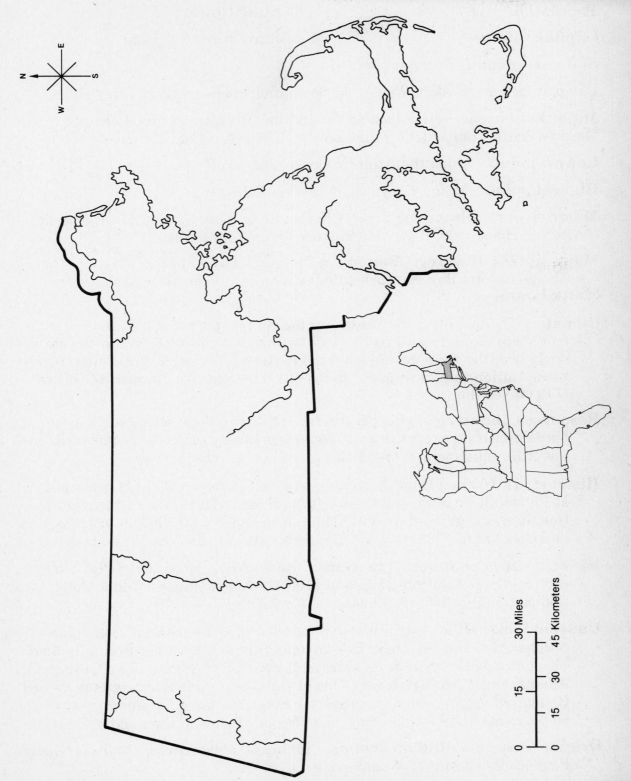

30 Miles

45 Kilometers

15   30

15   30

0   0   15

FACTS ABOUT
MASSACHUSETTS

Population: 5,871,000

Capital: Boston

State nickname: The Bay State

State flower: Mayflower

State bird: Chickadee

Largest cities: Boston, Worcester, Springfield, New Bedford, Cambridge

Major land areas: Appalachian Mountains, Berkshire Hills, Coastal Lowlands, Connecticut Valley Lowland, New England Upland

Lowest point: Along the Atlantic Ocean, sea level

Highest point: Mount Greylock, 3,491 feet (1,064 m)

Major rivers: Blackstone River, Charles River, Connecticut River, Hoosic River, Housatonic River, Merrimack River, Taunton River

Major bodies of water: Boston Bay, Buzzards Bay, Cape Cod Bay, Massachusetts Bay, Nantucket Sound, Quabbin Reservoir, Wachusett Reservoir

Climate: The average temperature in the central part of the state is 24°F (−4°C) in January and 70°F (21°C) in July. The western part of the state is slightly cooler than average and the eastern part, slightly warmer. Yearly precipitation ranges from 40 inches (100 cm) near the coast to 44 inches (112 cm) in the west.

Resources, industries, and products: Office and computing machines, textile machinery, printing and paper machinery, electronic equipment, scientific equipment, stone, fishing, milk, eggs, cranberries

History: In 1602 an English explorer visited the region. The Pilgrims landed at Plymouth in 1620, and the Puritans came in 1630. Massachusetts Bay Colony was chartered in 1691. The Revolutionary War began at Lexington and Concord in 1775. In 1788 Massachusetts became the sixth state.

Historic sites and other attractions: Bunker Hill Monument, Plimoth (Plymouth) Plantation, John and Priscilla Alden House, Walden Pond, Cape Cod National Seashore, Museum of Fine Arts

Unusual facts: Harvard University, founded in 1636, is the nation's oldest college. Alexander Graham Bell invented the telephone in Boston in 1876. Three Presidents were from Massachusetts: John Adams, John Quincy Adams, and John F. Kennedy. One of the lakes in Massachusetts is named Chaugoggagoggmanchaugagoggchaubunagungamaug. It means "You fish on your side and I'll fish on my side. Nobody fishes in the middle."

Original American Indian groups: Mahican, Massachuset, Nauset, Nipmuc, Pennacook, Pocomtuc, Wampanoag

MICHIGAN

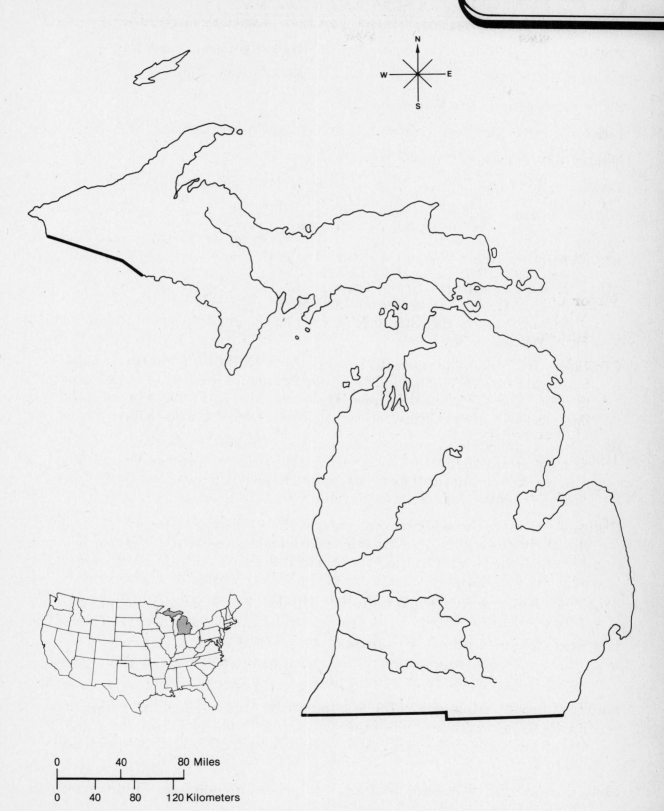

N
W — E
S

0   40   80 Miles

0   40   80   120 Kilometers

THE MAP BOOK

FACTS ABOUT
MICHIGAN

Population: 9,300,000

State flower: Apple blossom

Capital: Lansing

State bird: Robin

State nickname: The Wolverine State

Largest cities: Detroit, Grand Rapids, Warren, Flint, Lansing

Major land areas: Central Plains, Superior Upland

Lowest point: Along Lake Erie, 572 feet (174 m) above sea level

Highest point: Mount Curwood, 1,980 feet (604 m)

Major rivers: Detroit River, Escanaba River, Grand River, Kalamazoo River, Menominee River, Muskegon River, St. Clair River

Major bodies of water: Grand Traverse Bay, Green Bay, Houghton Lake, Lake Erie, Lake Gogebic, Lake Huron, Lake Michigan, Lake Saint Clair, Lake Superior, Saginaw Bay, Straits of Mackinac, Upper and Lower Tahquamenon Falls, Whitefish Bay

Climate: In January temperatures range from 15°F (−9°C) in the Upper Peninsula to 26°F (−3°C) in the Lower Peninsula. In July temperatures average 65°F (18°C) in the Upper Peninsula and 73°F (23°C) in the Lower Peninsula. Yearly precipitation ranges from about 25 to 35 inches (64 to 89 cm).

Resources, industries, and products: Automobiles, buses, trucks, nonelectrical machinery, tools, hardware, steel, food processing, chemicals, iron ore, copper, natural gas, salt, gypsum, peat, magnesium, fish, milk, cherries, apples, corn, honey, tourism

History: During the seventeenth century, the French explored and settled in the Michigan region. In 1763 the British took possession of the region after defeating the French in the French and Indian War. In 1787 Michigan was added to the Northwest Territory of the United States. It was later established as the Territory of Michigan, in 1805. In 1837 Michigan became the twenty-sixth state.

Historic sites and other attractions: Greenfield Village, Henry Ford Museum, Isle Royale National Park, the Soo Canals, Warren Dunes State Park, Mackinac Island, Pictured Rocks, Tahquamenon Falls

Unusual facts: Michigan is the leading producer of automobiles in the nation. Battle Creek produces more breakfast cereal than any other city in the world. One of the nation's largest salt mines lies about 1,000 feet (300 m) under Detroit.

Original American Indian groups: Chippewa, Menominee, Miami, Neutrals, Ottawa, Potawatomi

MINNESOTA

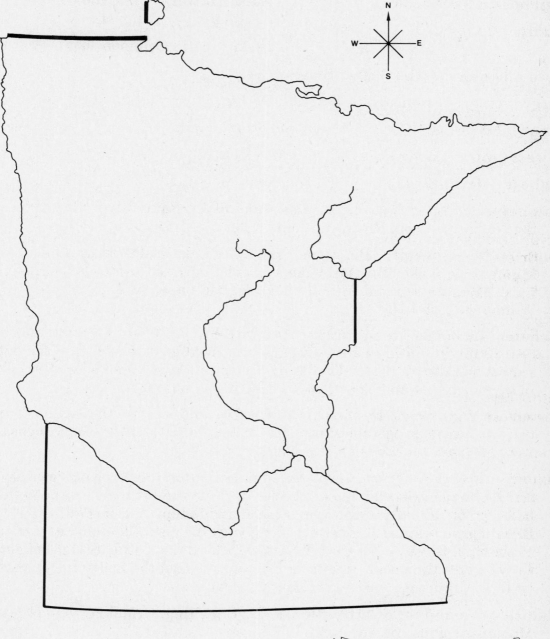

N
W   E
S

0   50   100 Miles

0   50   100   150 Kilometers

FACTS ABOUT
MINNESOTA

Population: 4,306,000

Capital: St. Paul

State flower: Pink and white lady's slipper

State bird: Common loon

State nickname: The Gopher State

Largest cities: Minneapolis, St. Paul, Duluth, Bloomington, Rochester

Major land areas: Central Plains, Superior Upland

Lowest point: Along Lake Superior, 602 feet (183 m) above sea level

Highest point: Eagle Mountain, 2,301 feet (701 m)

Major rivers: Minnesota River, Mississippi River, Rainy River, Red River of the North, St. Croix River, St. Louis River

Major bodies of water: Big Stone Lake, Cass Lake, Lake Itasca, Lake Minnetonka, Lake Superior, Lake Traverse, Lake of the Woods, Leech Lake, Minnehaha Falls, Mille Lacs Lake, Red Lake, Vermilion Lake, Winnibigoshish Lake

Climate: In January temperatures average 2°F (−17°C) in the north and 15°F (−9°C) in the south. In July temperatures average 68°F (20°C) in the north and 74°F (23°C) in the south. Yearly precipitation averages 19 inches (48 cm) in the northwest and 32 inches (81 cm) in the southeast.

Resources, industries, and products: Office and computing machines, meat packing, canned vegetables, iron ore, dairy products, cattle, corn, soybeans, wheat, apples, tourism, forest products, paper

History: French fur traders explored Minnesota in the seventeenth century, and the region was claimed by France. In 1763 the French gave the region to Great Britain after losing the French and Indian War. In 1783 Great Britain gave eastern Minnesota, along with the rest of the land east of the Mississippi River, to the United States. In 1803 the United States bought the western Minnesota area from France as part of the Louisiana Purchase. In 1858 Minnesota became the thirty-second state.

Historic sites and other attractions: Fort Snelling, Grand Portage National Monument, Pipestone National Monument, High Falls, Guthrie Theater, Voyageurs National Park, St. Paul Winter Carnival, Minnehaha Falls

Unusual facts: Minnesota has the world's largest open-pit iron mine. Part of Minnesota reaches farther north than any other state except Alaska. Henry Wadsworth Longfellow's poem "The Song of Hiawatha" made Minnehaha Falls famous.

Original American Indian groups: Cheyenne, Chippewa, Dakota, Iowa

MISSISSIPPI

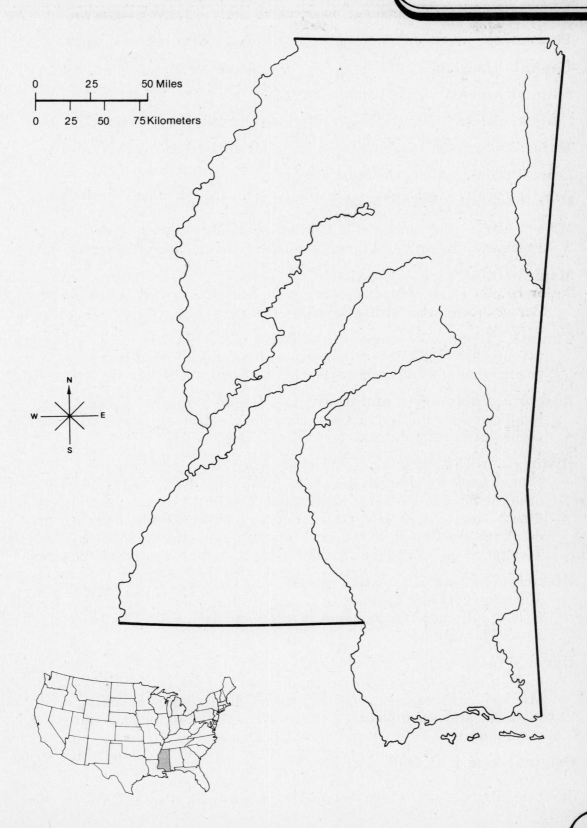

THE MAP BOOK

FACTS ABOUT
MISSISSIPPI

Population: 2,627,000

State flower: Magnolia

Capital: Jackson

State bird: Mockingbird

State nickname: The Magnolia State

Largest cities: Jackson, Biloxi, Meridian, Hattiesburg, Greenville

Major land areas: Gulf Coastal Plain, Mississippi Alluvial Plain

Lowest point: Along the coast, sea level

Highest point: Woodall Mountain, 806 feet (246 m)

Major rivers: Big Black River, Chickasawhay River, Mississippi River, Pascagoula River, Pearl River, Tombigbee River, Yazoo River

Major bodies of water: Arkabutla Lake (artificial), Enid Lake, Grenada Lake (artificial), Gulf of Mexico, Mississippi Sound, Pickwick Lake (artificial), Ross Barnett Reservoir, Sardis Lake (artificial)

Climate: In January temperatures average 48°F (9°C). In July temperatures average 82°F (28°C). Yearly precipitation ranges from 50 inches (130 cm) in the northwest to 65 inches (165 cm) in the southeast.

Resources, industries, and products: Shipbuilding, lumber and wood products, electronic equipment, chemicals, petroleum, food products, textiles, soybeans, sweet potatoes, cotton, rice, seafood

History: In 1540 Spanish explorers searched the region for gold. In 1682 a French explorer claimed the entire Mississippi River valley for France. This area included present-day Mississippi. The first European settlement was established in 1699. In 1763 the British took possession of the region after defeating the French in the French and Indian War. In 1798 the Mississippi Territory was formed. In 1817 Mississippi became the twentieth state.

Historic sites and other attractions: The Old Capital State Historical Museum, Fort Massachusetts, Vicksburg National Military Park, Petrified Forest, Jefferson Davis's home at Biloxi, mansions near Natchez, Florewood River Plantation

Unusual facts: The Petrified Forest contains giant stone trees dating back 30 million years. The word *Mississippi,* used by Indians to describe the Mississippi River, means "great water." Mississippi is a leading producer of soybeans and sweet potatoes. It has over 4,700 tree farms—more than any other state.

Original American Indian groups: Biloxi, Chickasaw, Choctaw, Natchez, Tunica, Yazoo

MISSOURI

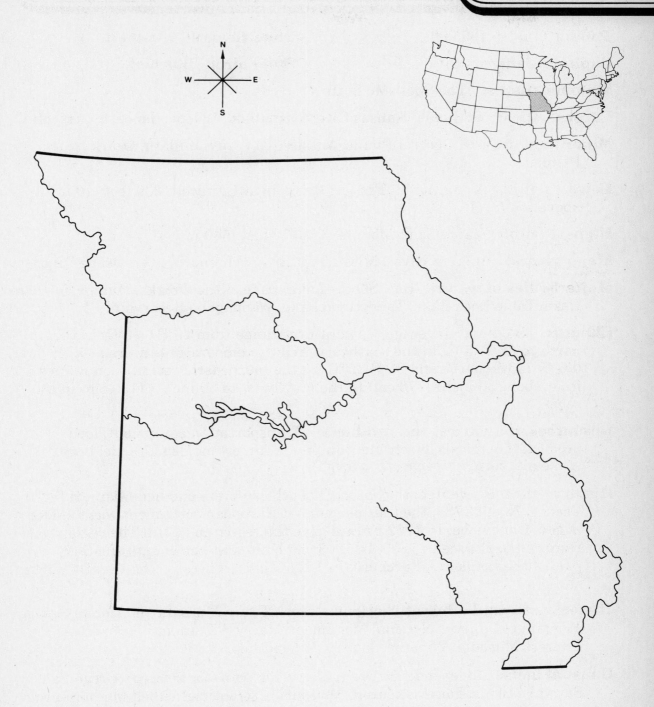

N
W——E
S

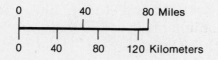

0   40   80 Miles

0   40   80   120 Kilometers

FACTS ABOUT
MISSOURI

Population: 5,139,000   **State flower:** Hawthorn

Capital: Jefferson City   **State bird:** Bluebird

State nickname: The Show Me State

Largest cities: St. Louis, Kansas City, Springfield, Independence, St. Joseph

Major land areas: Central Plains, Mississippi Alluvial Plain, Ozark Plateau

Lowest point: Along the St. Francis River, near Cardwell, 230 feet (70 m) above sea level

Highest point: Taum Sauk Mountain, 1,772 feet (540 m)

Major rivers: Current River, Mississippi River, Missouri River, Osage River

Major bodies of water: Bull Shoals Lake, Lake of the Ozarks, Pomme de Terre Lake, Table Rock Lake, Taneycomo Lake, Wappapello Reservoir (all artificial)

Climate: In January average temperatures range from 29°F (−2°C) in the north to 38°F (3°C) in the southeast. In July temperatures average 79°F (26°C) in the north and 81°F (27°C) in the southeast. Precipitation ranges from about 30 inches (76 cm) in the northwest to 50 inches (130 cm) in the southeast.

Resources, industries, and products: Transportation equipment, food products, chemicals, electronic equipment, limestone, lead, cattle, hogs, soybeans, corn, aerospace, tourism

History: In the seventeenth century, French explorers claimed Missouri for France. About 1735, the first permanent European settlement was founded in Ste. Genevieve. In 1762 France gave the region to Spain. The region was returned to France in 1800. In 1803 the United States bought the region as part of the Louisiana Purchase. In 1821 Missouri became the twenty-fourth state.

Historic sites and other attractions: Mark Twain Museum and Home, George Washington Carver National Monument, Harry S Truman Library, Pony Express Museum, Winston Churchill Memorial and Library

Unusual facts: Independence was the starting point for both the Oregon and Santa Fe trails. For this reason, Missouri is sometimes called Mother of the West. Missouri is one of two states that are bordered by eight states. (The other is Tennessee.) Gateway Arch in St. Louis, completed in 1965 and made of stainless steel, is the world's tallest monument. It is 630 feet (191 m) high. Missouri produces more lead than any other state.

Original American Indian groups: Fox, Missouri, Osage, Sauk

MONTANA

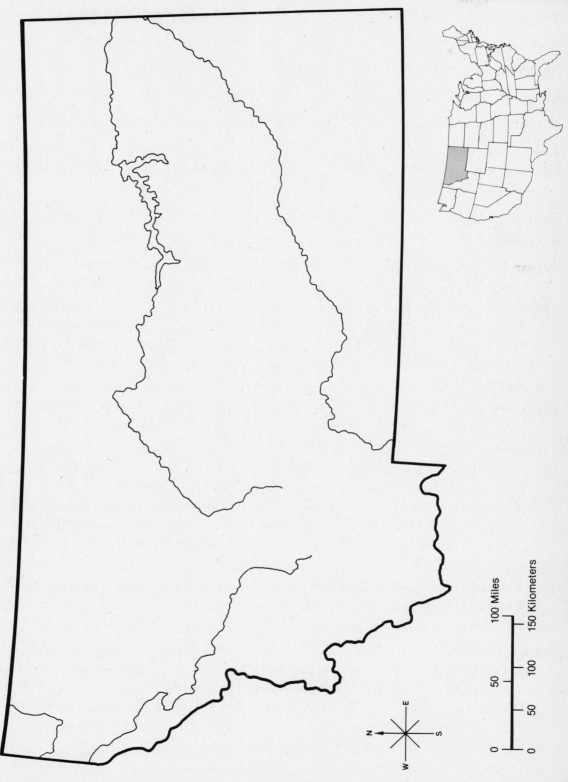

100 Miles

150 Kilometers

FACTS ABOUT
MONTANA

Population: 804,000

Capital: Helena

State flower: Bitterroot

State bird: Western meadowlark

State nickname: The Treasure State

Largest cities: Billings, Great Falls, Butte, Missoula, Helena

Major land areas: Great Plains, Rocky Mountains

Lowest point: Along the Kootenai River in Lincoln County, 1,800 feet (549 m) above sea level

Highest point: Granite Peak, 12,799 feet (3,901 m)

Major rivers: Clark Fork River, Kootenai River, Missouri River, Yellowstone River

Major bodies of water: Canyon Ferry Reservoir, Flathead Lake, Fort Peck Lake (artificial)

Climate: The average temperature in January is 20°F (−7°C) in the west and 14°F (−10°C) in the east. The average temperature in July is 64°F (18°C) in the west and 71°F (22°C) in the east. Average precipitation is 13 inches (933 cm) a year.

Resources, industries, and products: Food products, petroleum, natural gas, coal, copper, gold, silver, zinc, tourism, wood products and lumber, hogs, cattle, wheat, barley, hay, sugar beets, farm machinery

History: French fur trappers reached Montana in the eighteenth century, and Lewis and Clark passed through the region in 1805. The southern region was purchased from France as part of the Louisiana Purchase in 1803. Great Britain gave the northern region to the United States in 1846. In 1864 Montana Territory was established. In 1877 the Indian wars with the Sioux and Nez Perce Indians ended. In 1889 Montana became the forty-first state.

Historic sites and other attractions: Custer Battleground National Monument, Glacier National Park, Virginia City, Medicine Monument, Great Falls of the Missouri, Giant Springs at Great Falls, National Bison Range, Museum of the Plains Indian, Morrison Cave State Park

Unusual facts: Montana is the fourth-largest state in the nation. Butte Hill is the world's largest copper mine. Pompey's Pillar on the Yellowstone River was a famous landmark for pioneers going west. Montana is the only state drained by river systems that empty into the Gulf of Mexico, Hudson Bay, and the Pacific Ocean.

Original American Indian groups: Assiniboin, Atsina, Blackfoot, Crow, Kutenai, Salish

NEBRASKA

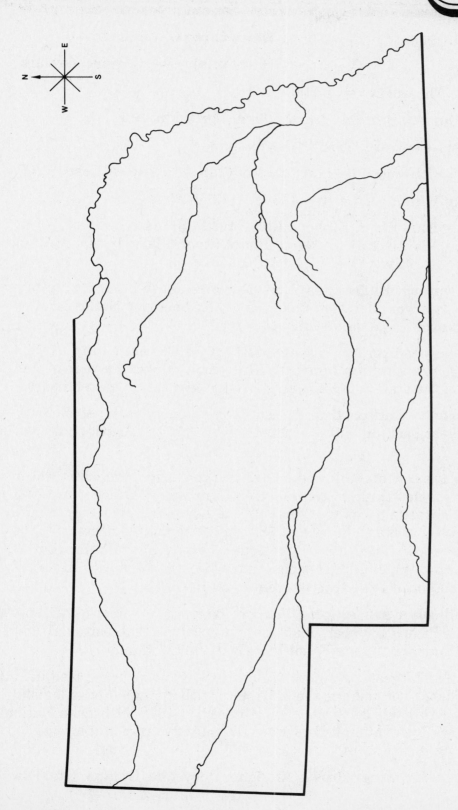

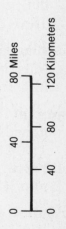

80 Miles

120 Kilometers

80

40

40

40

0

0

THE MAP BOOK

FACTS ABOUT
NEBRASKA

Population: 1,601,000

Capital: Lincoln

State flower: Goldenrod

State bird: Western meadowlark

State nickname: The Cornhusker State

Largest cities: Omaha, Lincoln, Grand Island, North Platte, Fremont

Major land areas: Central Plains, Great Plains

Lowest point: In Richardson County, 840 feet (256 m) above sea level

Highest point: In Kimball County, 5,426 feet (1,654 m)

Major rivers: Big Blue River, Elkhorn River, Little Blue River, Loup River, Missouri River, Niobrara River, North Platte River, Platte River, Republican River, South Platte River

Major bodies of water: Enders Reservoir, Harlan County Lake, Harry Strunk Lake, Jeffrey Reservoir, Johnson Lake, Lake McConaughy, Sutherland Reservoir, Swanson Lake (all artificial)

Climate: In January temperatures average 25°F (−4°C) and in July, 77°F (25°C). Average precipitation ranges from 12 inches (30 cm) a year in the western part of the state to 32 inches (81 cm) a year in the eastern part.

Resources, industries, and products: Electronics, chemicals, petroleum, natural gas, meat packing, dairy products, livestock feed, cattle, hogs, corn, wheat, flour

History: During the seventeenth and eighteenth centuries, French explorers and trappers traveled through Nebraska on their way to Oregon. In 1762 France gave Nebraska to Spain, as part of the Louisiana Territory. Spain then returned Nebraska to France in 1800, and the United States bought it in the Louisiana Purchase of 1803. Settlement began in the Nebraska Territory in 1854. When Congress passed the Kansas–Nebraska Act in 1867, Nebraska became the thirty-seventh state.

Historic sites and other attractions: Arbor Lodge, Scouts Rest Ranch, Stuhr Museum of the Prairie Pioneer, Toadstool Park, Homestead National Monument of America, Agate Fossil Beds National Monument

Unusual facts: The largest mammoth fossil ever found was unearthed in 1922 near North Platte. Nebraska is the only state with a single-house legislature. The first Arbor Day was celebrated in Nebraska in 1872. Nebraska National Forest and McKelvie National Forest are the only two national forests planted entirely by foresters.

Original American Indian groups: Arapaho, Cheyenne, Omaha, Oto, Pawnee, Ponca

NEVADA

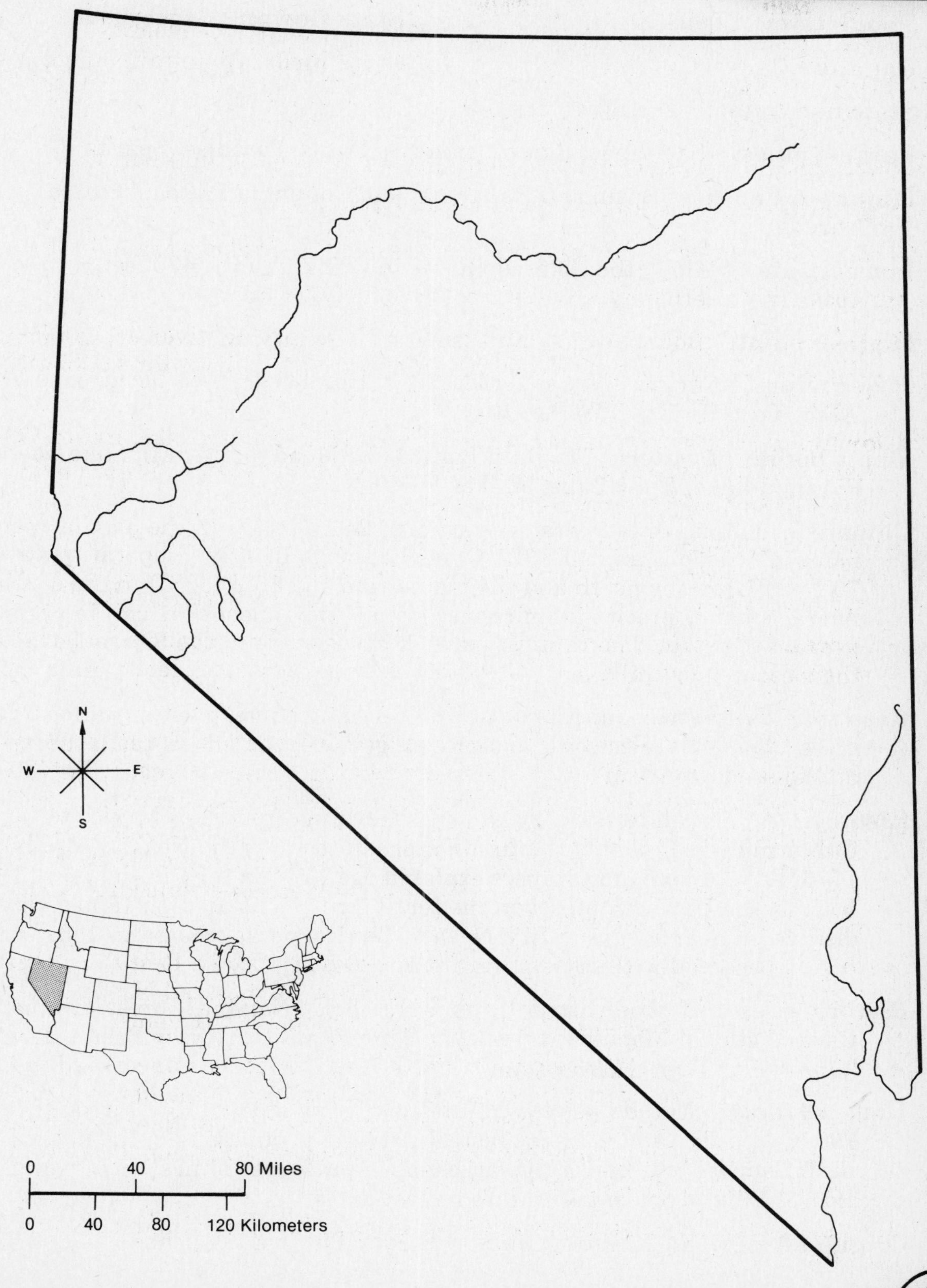

N
W   E
S

0   40   80 Miles

0   40   80   120 Kilometers

THE MAP BOOK

59

FACTS ABOUT
NEVADA

Population: 1,060,000

Capital: Carson City

State nickname: The Silver State

State flower: Sagebrush

State bird: Mountain bluebird

Largest cities: Las Vegas, Reno, North Las Vegas, Paradise, Sparks

Major land areas: Basin and Range Region, Columbia Plateau, Sierra Nevada

Lowest point: Along the Colorado River in Clark County, 470 feet (143 m) above sea level

Highest point: Boundary Peak in Esmeralda County, 13,143 feet (4,006 m)

Major rivers: Carson River, Colorado River, Humboldt River, Meadow Valley Wash, Truckee River, Walker River

Major bodies of water: Franklin Lake, Lake Mead (artificial), Lake Tahoe, Pyramid Lake, Ruby Lake, Walker Lake

Climate: In January temperatures average 24°F (−4°C) in the northern and mountain regions and 43°F (21°C) in the south. In July temperatures average 70°F (21°C) in the north and the mountains and 86°F (30°C) in the south. Average yearly precipitation ranges from 0 to 24 inches (61 cm) in various parts of the state. The rainiest parts of Nevada are in the Sierra Nevada and their eastern foothills.

Resources, industries, and products: Building stone, plaster, wallboard, glass, chemicals, electronic equipment, gold, copper, silver, cattle, sheep, alfalfa seeds, tourism

History: A Spanish missionary who was traveling from New Mexico to California was probably the first European to enter the Nevada region, in 1776. Fur traders and trappers explored the Nevada area in the early 1800s. In 1848 the United States won the territory from Mexico. In 1859 silver was discovered near Virginia City. Nevada Territory was created in 1861, and the region became the thirty-sixth state in 1864.

Historic sites and other attractions: Humboldt National Forest, Lehman Caves National Monument, Valley of Fire, Rhyolite, Geyser Basin, Lake Tahoe State Park, Hoover Dam

Unusual facts: Nevada has less rainfall than any other state. During the 1960s, Nevada had one of the fastest-growing populations in the nation. Ruth Copper Pit is one of the largest open-pit copper mines in the world. Hoover Dam is one of the world's largest dams.

Original American Indian groups: Paiute, Shoshoni, Washoe

NEW HAMPSHIRE

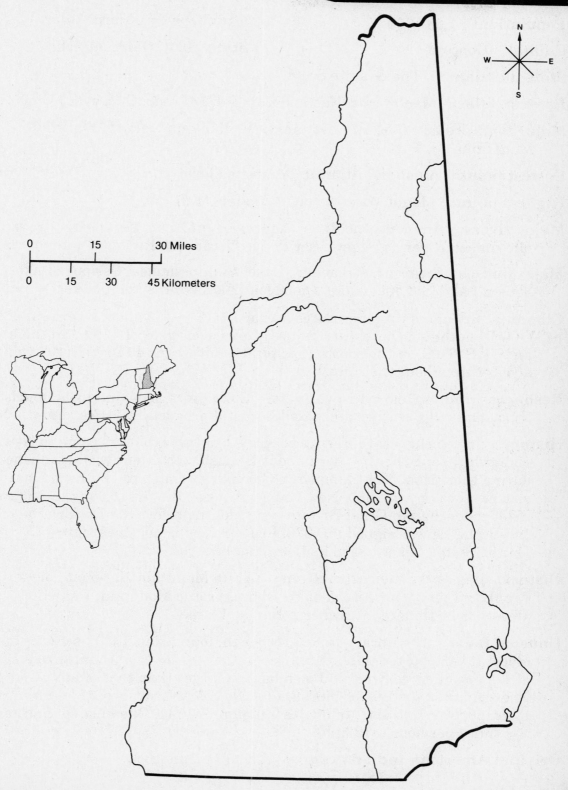

FACTS ABOUT NEW HAMPSHIRE

Population: 1,097,000

Capital: Concord

State nickname: The Granite State

Largest cities: Manchester, Nashua, Concord, Portsmouth, Dover

Major land areas: Coastal Lowlands, New England Upland, White Mountains

Lowest point: Along the Atlantic Ocean, sea level

Highest point: Mount Washington, 6,288 feet (1,917 m)

Major rivers: Ammonoosuc River, Androscoggin River, Connecticut River, Merrimack River, Pemigewasset River, Piscataqua River, Saco River

Major bodies of water: Great Bay, Lake Winnipesaukee, Ossippee Lake, Squam Lake, Sunapee Lake, Umbagog Lake, Winnisquam Lake

State flower: Purple lilac

State bird: Purple finch

Climate: In January temperatures average 16°F (−9°C) in the north and 22°F (−6°C) in the south. In July temperatures average 66°F (19°C) in the north and 70°F (21°C) in the south. Precipitation averages 42 inches (107 cm) a year throughout the state.

Resources, industries, and products: Electronics, machine tools, tourism, paper and pulp, leather and textiles, metal products, plastics, dairy products

History: In the early seventeenth century, English explorers came to New Hampshire, and the first permanent English settlement was established during the 1620s. New Hampshire Colony was chartered by King Charles II as a royal colony in 1680. New Hampshire was the first colony to declare its independence from Great Britain—six months before the Declaration of Independence was signed in 1776. In 1788 New Hampshire signed the United States Constitution and became the ninth state.

Historic sites and other attractions: White Mountain National Forest, Franklin Pierce Homestead at Hillsboro, Profile Mountain, Daniel Webster's birthplace, Strawberry Banke, Flume

Unusual facts: The library in Peterborough, founded in 1833, is one of the oldest tax-supported public libraries in the nation. New Hampshire's House of Representatives, with 400 members, is larger than that of any other state. The strongest winds ever measured at the Earth's surface, 188 miles per hour (303 kph), struck Mount Washington in 1934. One gust of wind reached 231 miles per hour (372 kph).

Original American Indian groups: Abnaki, Pennacook

NEW JERSEY

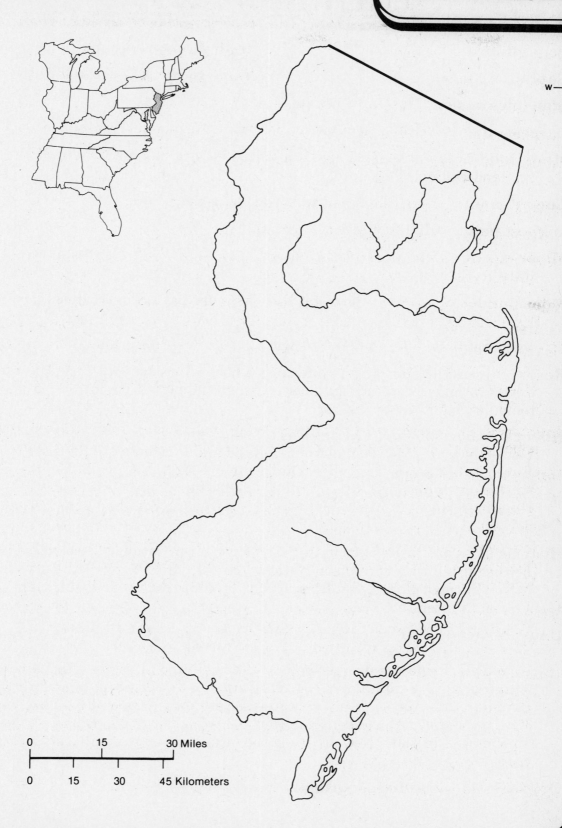

0   15   30 Miles

0   15   30   45 Kilometers

FACTS ABOUT
NEW JERSEY

Population: 7,720,000

Capital: Trenton

State nickname: The Garden State

State flower: Purple violet

State bird: Eastern goldfinch

Largest cities: Newark, Jersey City, Paterson, Elizabeth, Trenton

Major land areas: Appalachian Mountains, Atlantic Coastal Plain, New England Upland, Piedmont

Lowest point: Along the Atlantic Ocean, sea level

Highest point: High Point, 1,803 feet (550 m)

Major rivers: Delaware River, Hudson River, Mullica River, Passaic River, Raritan River

Major bodies of water: Barnegat Bay, Delaware Bay, Lake Hopatcong

Climate: In January temperatures average 30°F (−1°C). In July the average temperature is 73°F (23°C). Precipitation averages 46 inches (117 cm) a year.

Resources, industries, and products: Chemical production, food processing, electrical and electronic equipment, rubber and plastic products, textiles, tomatoes, potatoes, beans, corn

History: Giovanni da Verrazano was probably the first European to explore New Jersey, in 1524. People from Holland and Sweden were the first Europeans to settle there. The Dutch established the first permanent settlement in Bergen. In 1664 the English won control of the region. During the American Revolution, many battles were fought there. In 1787 New Jersey became the third state.

Historic sites and other attractions: Morristown National Historical Park, Barnegat Lighthouse, Edison National Historic Site, Princeton University, Walt Whitman House, Old Barracks in Trenton, Delaware Water Gap, Palisades Interstate Park

Unusual facts: The radio, electric light bulb, telegraph, and submarine were all invented in New Jersey. New Jersey leads the states in the production of chemicals. Princeton was the capital of the United States in 1783, and Trenton was the capital in 1784. The first game of organized baseball was played in Hoboken in 1846 between the New York Nine and the New York Knickerbockers. Alexander Hamilton was killed by Aaron Burr in a duel at Weehawken in 1804. New Jersey is the most densely populated state in the nation.

Original American Indian group: Delaware

NEW MEXICO

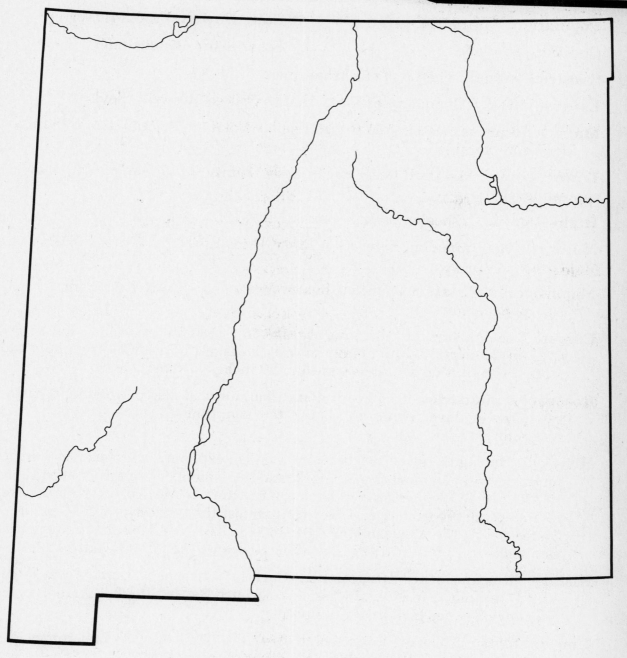

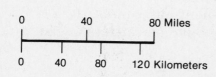

| 0 | 40 | 80 Miles |
| 0 | 40 | 80 | 120 Kilometers |

N
W   E
S

THE MAP BOOK

FACTS ABOUT
NEW MEXICO

Population: 1,510,000

Capital: Santa Fe

State flower: Yucca flower

State bird: Roadrunner

State nickname: The Land of Enchantment

Largest cities: Albuquerque, Santa Fe, Las Cruces, Roswell, Clovis

Major land areas: Basin and Range Region, Colorado Plateau, Great Plains, Rocky Mountains

Lowest point: Red Bluff Reservoir in Eddy County, 2,817 feet (859 m) above sea level

Highest point: Wheeler Peak in Taos County, 13,161 feet (4,011 m)

Major rivers: Canadian River, Gila River, Pecos River, Rio Grande, San Juan River

Major bodies of water: Conchas Reservoir, Elephant Butte Reservoir, Navajo Reservoir

Climate: In January temperatures average 55°F (13°C) in the south and 35°F (2°C) in the north. In July temperatures average 74°F (23°C) throughout the state. Precipitation averages less than 20 inches (51 cm) a year.

Resources, industries, and products: Coal, natural gas, petroleum, potash, sand, gravel, silver, uranium, copper, tourism, lumber, cattle, sheep, sorghum, hay, wheat, cotton

History: During the sixteenth century, Spanish explorers searched New Mexico for gold. Spain claimed the territory, and settlements were established there in 1598. In 1821 Spain surrendered the territory to Mexico, after Mexico won its independence from Spain. Mexico then lost the territory to the United States during the Mexican War (1846–1848). The New Mexico Territory was established in 1850. In 1912 New Mexico became the forty-seventh state.

Historic sites and other attractions: Carlsbad Caverns National Park, Puye Cliff Dwellings, San Miguel Mission, Glorietta Battle Site, Los Alamos Bradbury Science Hall and Museum

Unusual facts: The first atomic bomb was built at Los Alamos Laboratory and exploded near Alamogordo. The oldest highway in the United States is El Camino Real, first used in 1581. The world's largest known system of caves is Carlsbad Caverns. The oldest government building in the United States is the Palace of the Governors, built by Spanish settlers in Santa Fe in 1610.

Original American Indian groups: Apache, Navajo, Pueblo (Keresan, Shoshoni, Zuni)

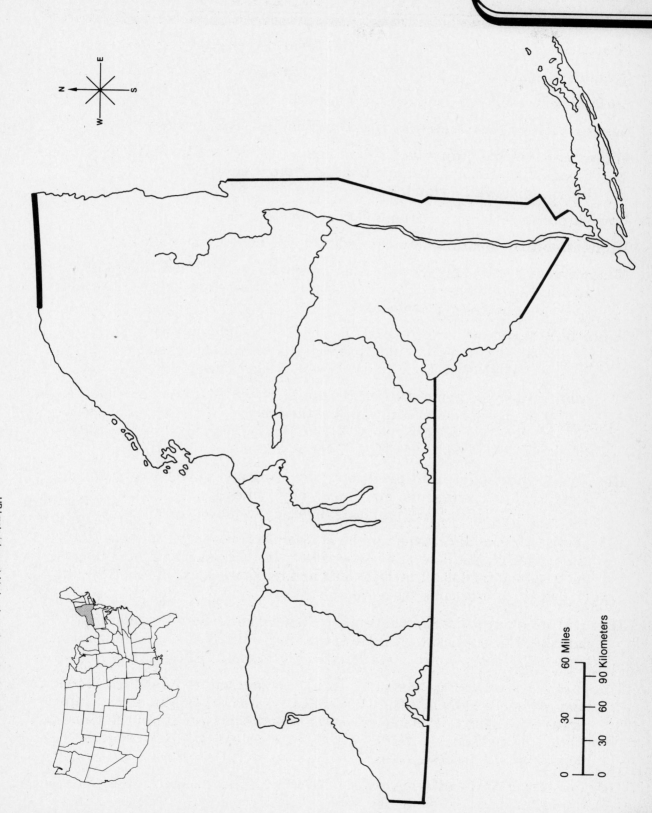

60 Miles

90 Kilometers

FACTS ABOUT
NEW YORK

Population: 17,898,000

Capital: Albany

State nickname: The Empire State

State flower: Rose

State bird: Bluebird

Largest cities: New York City, Buffalo, Rochester, Yonkers, Syracuse

Major land areas: Adirondack Mountains, Appalachian Mountains, Appalachian Plateau, Atlantic Coastal Plain, Central Plains, Hudson-Mohawk Lowland, New England Upland

Lowest point: Along the Atlantic Ocean, sea level

Highest point: Mount Marcy, 5,344 feet (1,629 m)

Major rivers: Allegheny River, Delaware River, East River, Genesee River, Hudson River, Mohawk River, Niagara River, Oswego River, St. Lawrence River, Seneca River, Susquehanna River

Major bodies of water: Allegheny Reservoir, Chautauqua Lake, Finger Lakes, Lake Champlain, Lake Erie, Lake George, Lake Oneida, Lake Ontario, Lake Placid, Long Island Sound, Niagara Falls, Saranac Lake

Climate: In January temperatures average 17°F (−8°C) in the Adirondacks and 32°F (0°C) on the coastal plain. In July the average temperatures are 66°F (19°C) in the Adirondacks and 74°F (23°C) on the coastal plain. Precipitation ranges from 32 to 54 inches (81 to 137 cm) a year.

Resources, industries, and products: Printing and publishing, medical and photographic instruments, machinery, electronics, tourism, industrial equipment, textiles, dairy products, banking, finance, communications

History: Henry Hudson explored the Hudson River in 1609. Dutch settlers established New Amsterdam (New York City) in 1625. The English seized the territory from the Dutch in 1664 and renamed the area New York. In 1778 New York became the eleventh state.

Historic sites and other attractions: Niagara Falls, Fort Ticonderoga, Saratoga National Historical Park, Statue of Liberty National Monument, United Nations, Empire State Building, Metropolitan Museum of Art

Unusual facts: The first woman's suffrage convention in the United States was held in Seneca Falls in 1848. New York City was the capital of the United States from 1785 to 1790. New York City is the largest city in the United States and the sixth-largest city in the world. It is one of the world's biggest and busiest seaports.

Original American Indian groups: Delaware, Erie, Iroquois, Mahican, Mohegan, Montauk, Neutrals, Sapono, Tuscarora, Tutelo, Wappinger

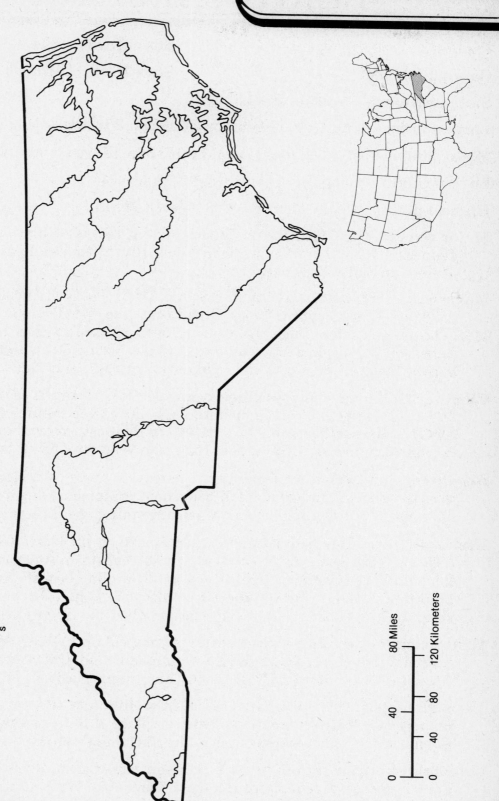

N E S W

80 Miles

40

120 Kilometers

80

40

0   0

FACTS ABOUT
NORTH CAROLINA

Population: 6,526,000

State flower: Flowering dogwood

Capital: Raleigh

State bird: Cardinal

State nickname: The Tar Heel State

Largest cities: Charlotte, Greensboro, Raleigh, Winston-Salem, Durham

Major land areas: Atlantic Coastal Plain, Blue Ridge Mountains, Piedmont

Lowest point: Along the Atlantic coast, sea level

Highest point: Mount Mitchell, 6,684 feet (2,037 m)

Major rivers: Cape Fear River, Catawba River, Hiwassee River, Little Tennessee River, Nantahala River, Neuse River, Pee Dee River, Roanoke River, Tar River, Yadkin River

Major bodies of water: Albemarle Sound, Badin Lake (artificial), Blewett Falls Lake (artificial), Fontana Lake, High Rock Lake (artificial), B. Everett Jordan Lake, Lake Gaston, Lake Hickory (artificial), Lake Hiwassee (artificial), Lake James (artificial), Lake Mattamuskeet, Lake Norman (artificial), Lake Phelps, Lake Tillery (artificial), Pamlico Sound, W. Kerr Scott Reservoir

Climate: In January temperatures average 48°F (9°C) in the southeast and 28°F (−2°C) in the western mountains. In July temperatures average 80°F (27°C) in the southeast and 65°F (19°C) in the western mountains. Precipitation averages 52 inches (131 cm) a year throughout the state.

Resources, industries, and products: Textiles, chemicals, electronics, tobacco, tourism, industrial and household equipment, furniture, phosphate rock, feldspar, lithium, mica, granite, gravel, lumber, corn

History: In 1524 Giovanni da Verrazano landed on the North Carolina coast. In 1585 the English established their first settlement in America at Roanoke Island. In the seventeenth century, North Carolina became an English proprietary colony. In 1776 the colony claimed its independence and wrote a state constitution. In 1789 North Carolina became the twelfth state.

Historic sites and other attractions: Alamance Battlefield, Wright Brothers National Memorial, Tryon Palace, Ocracoke Island, Chimney Rock, Grandfather Mountain, Great Smoky Mountains National Park

Unusual facts: The University of North Carolina was the nation's first state university. The first airplane flight took place at Kitty Hawk in 1903. Colonists settled on Roanoke Island in 1587, but later mysteriously vanished.

Original American Indian groups: Cape Fear, Cheraw, Chowanoc, Coree, Enox Hatteras, Machapunga, Shakori, Tuscarora, Weapemeoc

NORTH DAKOTA

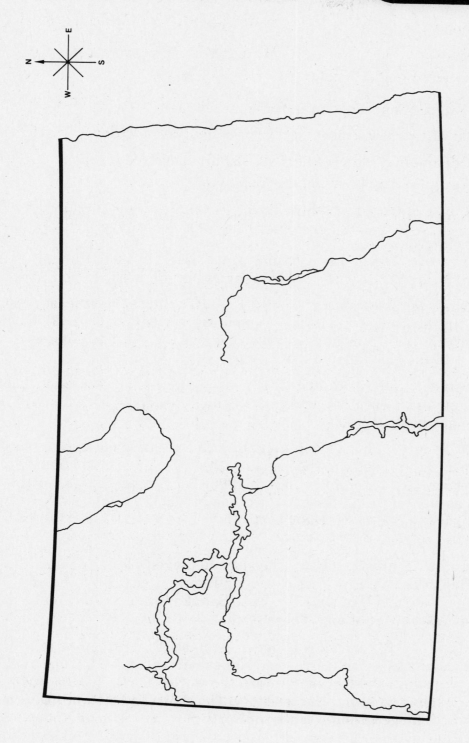

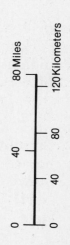

80 Miles

120 Kilometers

| | | | | |
40 80
0 40
0

THE MAP BOOK

FACTS ABOUT
NORTH DAKOTA

Population: 663,000

State flower: Wild prairie rose

Capital: Bismarck

State bird: Western meadowlark

State nickname: The Flickertail State

Largest cities: Fargo, Bismarck, Grand Forks, Minot, Jamestown

Major land areas: Central Plains, Great Plains, Red River Valley

Lowest point: In Pembina County, 750 feet (229 m) above sea level

Highest point: White Butte, 3,506 feet (1,069 m)

Major rivers: James River, Little Missouri River, Missouri River, Red River, Souris River

Major bodies of water: Devils Lake, Jamestown Reservoir, Lake Darling (artificial), Lake Oahe (artificial), Lake Sakakawea (artificial), Long Lake

Climate: In January temperatures average 3°F (−16°C) in the northeast and 14°F (−10°C) in the southwest. In July temperatures average 69°F (21°C) in the north and 72°F (22°C) in the south. Throughout the state, precipitation averages 15 to 18 inches (38 to 46 cm) a year.

Resources, industries, and products: Farm equipment, food processing, oil and natural gas, lignite coal, tourism, cattle, hogs, sheep, wheat, flaxseed, barley, rye, sugar beets, potatoes

History: In 1682 France claimed the region, but explorers did not arrive there until 1738. In 1762 France gave the region west of the Missouri to Spain. Spain then returned the land to France in 1800. The United States bought the territory as part of the Louisiana Purchase in 1803. By 1812 settlers began moving to the region. In 1889 North Dakota became the thirty-ninth state.

Historic sites and other attractions: Theodore Roosevelt National Memorial Park in the Badlands, Writing Rock, Burning Lignite Beds, Knife River Indian Villages National Historic Site, Lake Sakakawea, Fort Abraham Lincoln State Park, International Peace Garden

Unusual facts: The Red River Valley is one of the most fertile regions in the world. North Dakota is usually second to Kansas in wheat production. Garrison Dam is one of the largest dams in the world. North Dakota was named for the Sioux Indians of the territory. The Sioux Indian word *Dakota* means "friends." The geographic center of North America is near Rugby. North Dakota has a larger percentage of agricultural workers than any other state.

Original American Indian groups: Arikara, Hidatsa, Mandan

OHIO

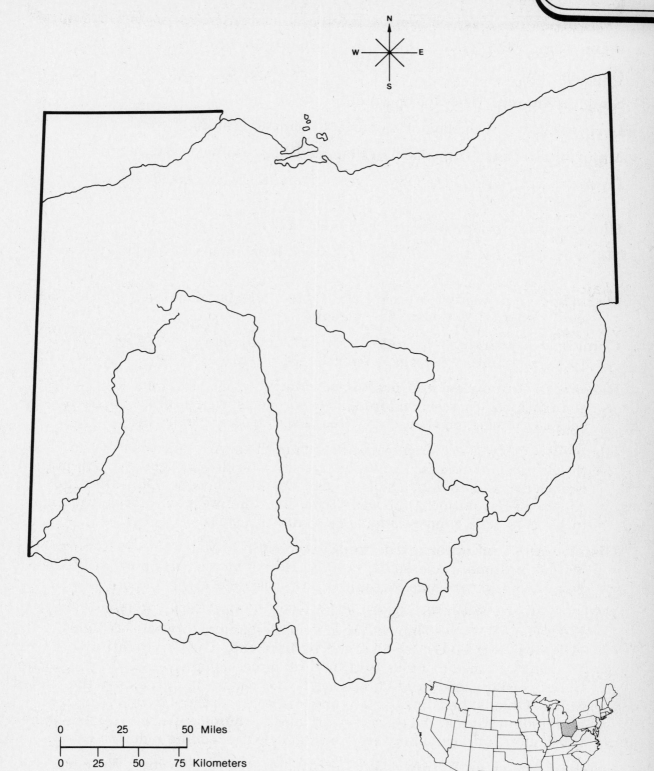

N
W   E
S

0   25   50   Miles

0   25   50   75   Kilometers

FACTS ABOUT
OHIO

Population: 10,872,000   **State flower:** Scarlet carnation

Capital: Columbus   **State bird:** Cardinal

State nickname: The Buckeye State

Largest cities: Cleveland, Columbus, Cincinnati, Toledo, Akron

Major land areas: Appalachian Plateau, Bluegrass Region, Central Plains

Lowest point: Along the Ohio River in Hamilton County, 433 feet (132 m) above sea level

Highest point: Campbell Hill, 1,550 feet (472 m)

Major rivers: Maumee River, Miami River, Muskingum River, Ohio River, Scioto River

Major bodies of water: Dillon Lake, Grand Lake (artificial), Lake Erie, Miami and Erie Canal, Ohio and Erie Canal

Climate: Temperatures average 31°F (−1°C) in January and 74°F (23°C) in July. Precipitation averages 37 inches (94 cm) a year.

Resources, industries, and products: Machine tools, farm machinery, bus and truck bodies, steel and iron, metal products, rubber products, meat packing, bricks and tiles, dairy products, corn, soybeans, wheat

History: Ohio was explored by the French in the seventeenth century. In 1763 the British won possession of the territory after defeating the French in the French and Indian War. The United States won control of Ohio after the American Revolution. Ohio was part of the Northwest Territory established in 1787. In 1803 Ohio became the seventeenth state.

Historic sites and other attractions: Adena State Memorial, Great Serpent Mound, National Professional Football Hall of Fame, Schoenbrunn Village, Fort Recovery, Air Force Museum, Neil Armstrong Air and Space Museum

Unusual facts: Seven Presidents were born in Ohio: Ulysses S. Grant, Rutherford B. Hayes, James A. Garfield, Benjamin Harrison, William McKinley, Warren G. Harding, and William Taft. The Cincinnati Red Stockings, formed in 1869, were the first professional baseball team. Oberlin College, established in 1833, was the first coeducational college in the United States. Ohio is the home of many inventions, including the process of aluminum refining, the cash register, and the automobile self-starter. Ohio is third, after California and New York, among the leading industrial states.

Original American Indian groups: Erie, Mosopelea, Shawnee, Wyandot (Huron)

OKLAHOMA

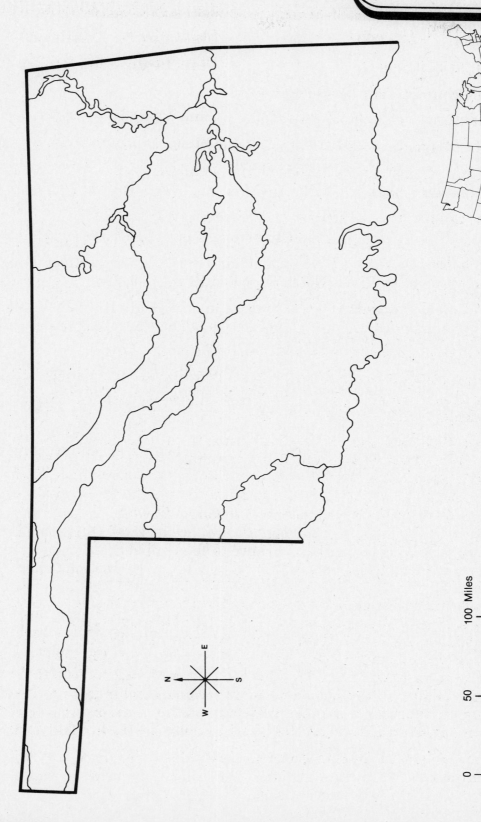

100 Miles

150 Kilometers

50

100

50

50

0

0

THE MAP BOOK

FACTS ABOUT
OKLAHOMA

Population: 3,263,000

State flower: Mistletoe

Capital: Oklahoma City

State bird: Scissor-tailed flycatcher

State nickname: The Sooner State

Largest cities: Oklahoma City, Tulsa, Lawton, Norman, Enid

Major land areas: Central Plains, Great Plains, Ozark Plateau, Ouachita Mountains, Red River Valley Region

Lowest point: Along the Little River in McCurtain County, 287 feet (87 m) above sea level

Highest point: Black Mesa in Cimarron County, 4,973 feet (1,516 m)

Major rivers: Arkansas River, Canadian River, Cimarron River, Neosho River, North Canadian River, North Fork Red River, Red River

Major bodies of water: Fort Gibson Lake (artificial), Keystone Lake, Lake Eufaula, Lake Hudson (artificial), Lake O'The Cherokees (artificial), Lake Texoma (artificial), Robert S. Kerr Reservoir

Climate: In January temperatures average 39°F (4°C) throughout Oklahoma. In July the average temperature throughout the state is 83°F (28°C). The average yearly precipitation ranges from 15 inches (38 cm) in the Panhandle, the western part of Oklahoma, to 50 inches (130 cm) in the southeast.

Resources, industries, and products: Petroleum products, machinery, food products, tools, manufacturing, rubber products, coal, petroleum and natural gas, cattle, wheat, cotton

History: In 1682 the French claimed the area. In 1762 France transferred the region to Spain, which returned it to France in 1800. Oklahoma (minus its Panhandle) was then sold by France to the United States as part of the Louisiana Purchase of 1803. The eastern territory was controlled by Indian groups until after the Civil War (1861–1865). In 1907 Oklahoma became the forty-sixth state.

Historic sites and other attractions: Will Rogers Memorial, Washita Battlefield, Woolaroc Museum, Creek Capital, Dinosaur Quarry, National Cowboy Hall of Fame and Western Heritage Center, Tsa-La-Gi Indian Village

Unusual facts: In 1889, when Oklahoma was opened to settlers, 50,000 people moved there in a single day. Oklahoma is home to more American Indians than any other state except Arizona. The state capitol in Oklahoma City stands on a major oil field.

Original American Indian groups: Arapaho, Comanche, Kichai, Kiowa, Kiowa Apache, Okmulgee, Osage, Wichita

OREGON

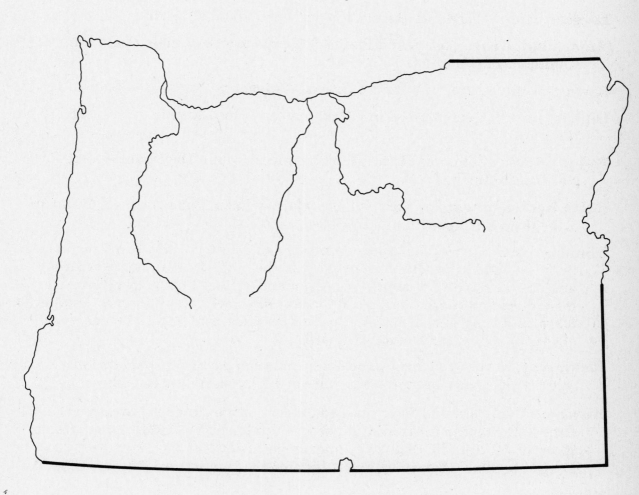

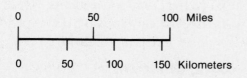

0   50   100 Miles

0   50   100   150 Kilometers

THE MAP BOOK

77

FACTS ABOUT
OREGON

Population: 2,741,000

State flower: Oregon grape

Capital: Salem

State bird: Western meadow lark

State nickname: The Beaver State

Largest cities: Portland, Eugene, Salem, Springfield, Corvallis

Major land areas: Basin and Range Region, Cascade Range, Coast Ranges, Columbia Plateau

Lowest point: Along the Pacific Ocean, sea level

Highest point: Mount Hood in Clackamas and Hood River counties, 11,235 feet (3,424 m)

Major rivers: Columbia River, Deschutes River, John Day River, Snake River, Willamette River

Major bodies of water: Crater Lake, Harney Lake, Lake Owyhee, Malheur Lake, Upper Klamath Lake, Wallowa Lake

Climate: In January temperatures average 45°F (7°C) in western Oregon and 27°F (−3°C) in the southeastern part of the state. In July temperatures average 60°F (16°C) in western Oregon and 72°F (22°C) in the southeast. Yearly precipitation averages 40 inches (100 cm) in the Willamette Valley, 50 to 75 inches (130 to 191 cm) in the Cascades, and 6 to 12 inches (15 to 30 cm) in much of eastern Oregon.

Resources, industries, and products: Lumber and wood products, food processing, paper products, tourism, metals, fishing, cattle, wheat

History: Explorers may have reached Oregon in the sixteenth century. The first settlement, a fur-trading post, was established in 1811 by John Jacob Astor at Astoria. In 1843 large migrations of settlers began. In 1848 Oregon became a territory, and it became the thirty-third state in 1859.

Historic sites and other attractions: Columbia River Gorge, Fort Clatsop National Memorial, Crater Lake National Park, Mount Hood National Forest, Picture Gorge, Sea Lion Caves, Shakespeare Festival

Unusual facts: Oregon leads the nation in timber production. The name *Oregon* comes from the French word meaning "hurricane," which was used to describe the mighty Columbia River. The Columbia River was named after the ship of an early explorer, Captain Robert Gray, who sailed into the river in 1792. Crater Lake is the deepest lake in the United States. Its depth is 1,932 feet (589 m), and it lies in the crater of an extinct volcano.

Original American Indian groups: Calapooya, Chastacosta, Chinook, Clackamas, Klamath, Modoc, Siuslaw, Takelma, Tillamook, Tuturui

PENNSYLVANIA

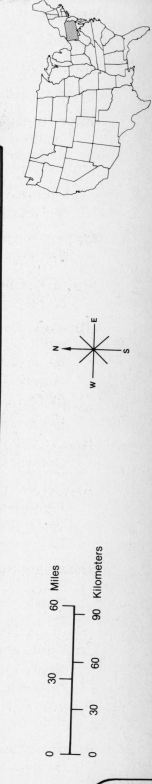

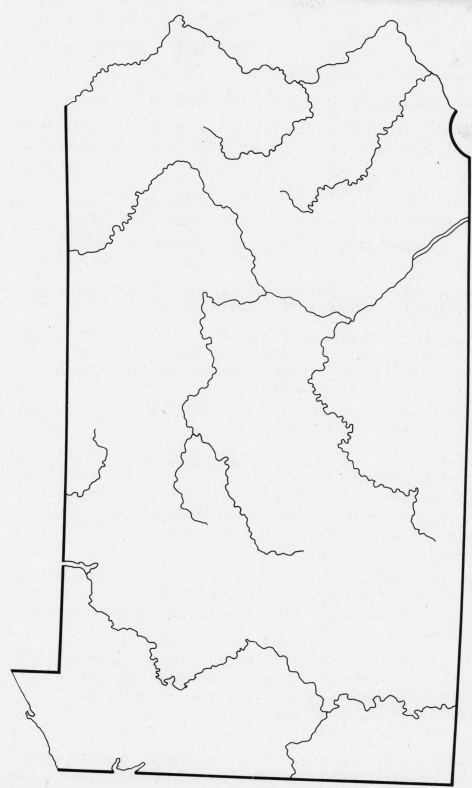

Miles

Kilometers

60

90

30

60

30

30

0

0

THE MAP BOOK

FACTS ABOUT
PENNSYLVANIA

Population: 12,027,000

State flower: Mountain laurel

Capital: Harrisburg

State bird: Ruffed grouse

State nickname: The Keystone State

Largest cities: Philadelphia, Pittsburgh, Erie, Allentown, Scranton

Major land areas: Appalachian Mountains, Appalachian Plateau, Atlantic Coastal Plain, Blue Ridge Mountains, Central Plains, New England Upland, Piedmont

Lowest point: Along the Delaware River, sea level

Highest point: Mount Davis in Somerset County, 3,213 feet (979 m)

Major rivers: Allegheny River, Delaware River, Juniata River, Lehigh River, Monongahela River, Ohio River, Schuylkill River, Susquehanna River

Major bodies of water: Allegheny Reservoir, Lake Erie, Lake Wallenpaupack, Pymatuning Reservoir, Raystown Lake (artificial)

Climate: In January temperatures average 26°F (-3°C) in the north and 34°F (1°C) in the southeast. In July temperatures average 70°F (21°C) in the northwest and 77°F (25°C) in the southeast. Precipitation averages 42 inches (107 cm) a year throughout the state.

Resources, industries, and products: Steel and pig iron, electrical and nonelectrical machinery, chemicals, food products, coal, dairy products

History: In 1643 Swedish settlers established a colony on Tinicum Island, near Philadelphia. The Dutch captured the region from the Swedes in 1655, and the English took control of the area in 1664. In 1681 Pennsylvania was given to William Penn. The Declaration of Independence was adopted by the 13 colonies in Philadelphia in 1776. In 1787 Pennsylvania became the second state.

Historic sites and other attractions: Independence Hall National Historical Park, Gettysburg National Military Park, Valley Forge, Pine Creek Gorge, Hawk Mountain Bird Sanctuary, Rockville Bridge, Pennsylvania Farm Museum of Landis Valley, Mummers' Parade on New Year's Day

Unusual facts: Pennsylvania leads the nation in steel production. KDKA, started in 1920, was one of the first radio stations in the country. The Pennsylvania Turnpike was the nation's first paved road. The world's largest chocolate factory is in Hershey. The Bank of North America in Philadelphia, dating from 1781, is the oldest bank in the United States.

Original American Indian groups: Delaware, Erie, Honniasont, Iroquois, Saluda, Saponi, Shawnee, Susquehanna, Tuscarora, Tutelo, Wenrohronon

RHODE ISLAND

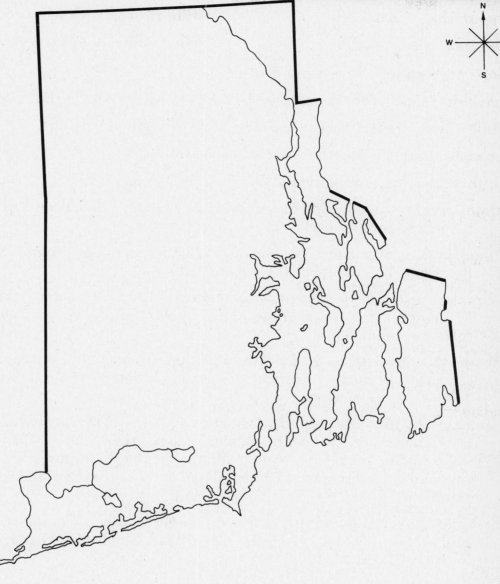

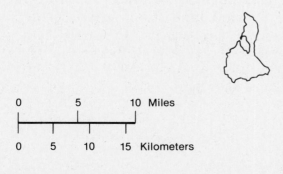

0   5   10 Miles

0   5   10   15 Kilometers

THE MAP BOOK

FACTS ABOUT
RHODE ISLAND

Population: 995,000   **State flower:** Violet

Capital: Providence   **State bird:** Rhode Island red (chicken)

State nickname: The Ocean State

Largest cities: Providence, Warwick, Cranston, Pawtucket, East Providence

Major land areas: Coastal Lowlands, New England Upland

Lowest point: Along the Atlantic coast, sea level

Highest point: Jerimoth Hill, 812 feet (247 m)

Major rivers: Blackstone River, Pawcatuck River, Providence River, Sakonnet River, Seekonk River, Woonasquatucket River

Major bodies of water: Narragansett Bay, Rhode Island Sound, Scituate Reservoir, Watchaug Pond, Worden Pond

Climate: In January temperatures average 30°F (−1°C) throughout the state. In July temperatures average 70°F (21°C). Precipitation averages 44 inches (112 cm) a year.

Resources, industries, and products: Jewelry and silverware, metal products, chemicals, electrical equipment, rubber products, textiles, fishing, dairy products, tourism

History: In 1524 Giovanni da Verrazano sailed into Narragansett Bay. The Dutch navigator Adriaen Block also explored the region in 1614. Providence was founded in 1636 by Roger Williams. In 1644 Williams got a charter from England for the colony of Rhode Island. In 1790 Rhode Island became the thirteenth state.

Historic sites and other attractions: Gilbert Stuart's birthplace, Old Stone Mill, General Nathanael Greene homestead, Slater Mill Historic Site, Newport, Block Island

Unusual facts: Rhode Island is the smallest state and is therefore often called Little Rhody. It has the longest official name of any state: State of Rhode Island and Providence Plantations. Rhode Island was the first of the original 13 colonies to declare independence from Great Britain. Touro Synagogue, built in 1763, is the oldest synagogue in the United States still in use today. Providence is the leading center of jewelry manufacturing in the nation. The Slater Mill, built in 1793 in Pawtucket, was one of North America's first textile mills.

Original American Indian groups: Narragansett, Niantic (Eastern), Nipmuc, Pequot, Wampanoag

SOUTH CAROLINA

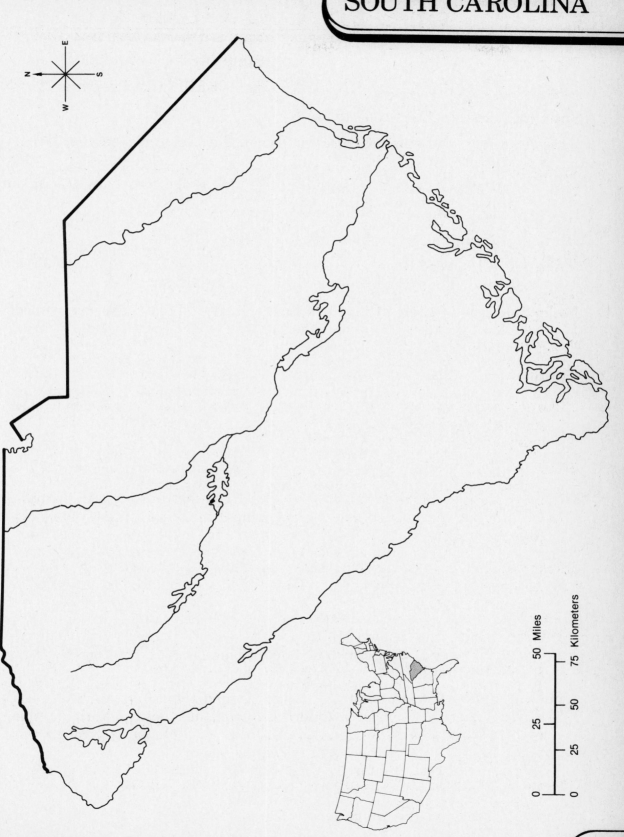

N E S W

50 Miles

75 Kilometers

50

25

25

25

0

0

THE MAP BOOK

FACTS ABOUT
SOUTH CAROLINA

Population: 3,493,000

Capital: Columbia

State nickname: The Palmetto State

State flower: Carolina jessamine

State bird: Carolina wren

Largest cities: Columbia, Charleston, North Charleston, Greenville, Spartanburg

Major land areas: Atlantic Coastal Plain, Blue Ridge Mountains, Piedmont

Lowest point: Along the Atlantic Ocean, sea level

Highest point: Sassafras Mountain, 3,560 feet (1,085 m)

Major rivers: Broad River, Chattooga River, Congaree River, Edisto River, Pee Dee River, Saluda River, Santee River, Savannah River

Major bodies of water: Clark Hill Lake, Hartwell Lake, Lake Greenwood, Lake Marion, Lake Moultrie, Lake Murray, Lake Wateree, Lake Wylie (all artificial)

Climate: In January temperatures average 51°F (11°C) in the south and 41°F (5°C) in the northwest. In July temperatures average 81°F (27°C) in the south and 72°F (22°C) in the northwest. Precipitation averages 45 inches (114 cm) a year.

Resources, industries, and products: Tourism, textiles, chemicals, machinery, clothing, soybeans, corn, cotton, peaches

History: In 1521 Spanish explorers reached the coastline of South Carolina. The English established the first permanent settlement in 1670 on Albemarle Point. In 1680 that colony moved to Charleston. In time, the name of South Carolina came into use for the southern part of the colony. The northern settlements became North Carolina. In 1788 South Carolina became the eighth state.

Historic sites and other attractions: Fort Sumter National Monument, Kings Mountain National Military Park, Cypress Gardens, Fort Moultrie, Cowpens National Battlefield, Middleton Place Gardens, Hilton Head Island, Windmill Point, Myrtle Beach, Charleston Museum

Unusual facts: It was in South Carolina, around 1685, that rice was first raised successfully in North America. One of the oldest museums in the country is the Charleston Museum, founded in 1773. South Carolina was the first state to withdraw from the Union before the Civil War. The Civil War began at Fort Sumter on April 12, 1861. South Carolina is a leader among the states in the production of textiles and peaches.

Original American Indian groups: Catawba, Cusabo

SOUTH DAKOTA

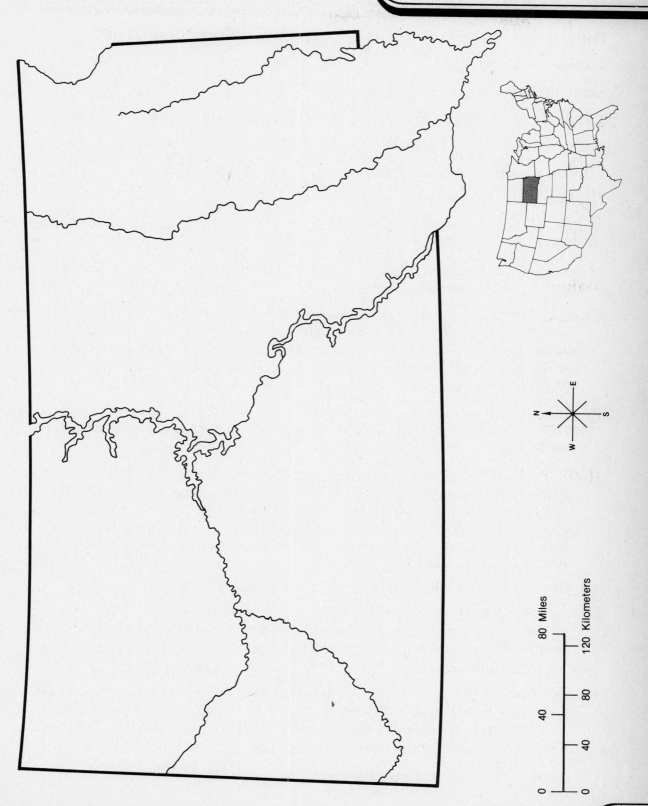

80 Miles

120 Kilometers

80

40

40

0   0

FACTS ABOUT
SOUTH DAKOTA

Population: 715,000

State flower: American pasqueflower

Capital: Pierre

State bird: Ring-necked pheasant

State nickname: The Sunshine State

Largest cities: Sioux Falls, Rapid City, Aberdeen, Watertown, Brookings

Major land areas: Black Hills, Central Plains, Great Plains

Lowest point: Big Stone Lake, 962 feet (293 m) above sea level

Highest point: Harney Peak, 7,242 feet (2,207 m)

Major rivers: Belle Fourche River, Big Sioux River, Cheyenne River, James River, Missouri River

Major bodies of water: Lake Francis Case, Lake Oahe, Lake Sharpe, Lewis and Clark Lake (all artificial)

Climate: In January average temperatures range from 10°F (−12°C) in the northeast to 22°F (−6°C) in the southwest. In July average temperatures range from 68°F (20°C) in the Black Hills to 78°F (26°C) throughout the rest of the state. Precipitation ranges from 13 inches (33 cm) in the northwest to 25 inches (64 cm) in the southeast.

Resources, industries, and products: Food products, machinery, cattle, hogs, lambs, sheep, geese, alfalfa seed, barley, flaxseed, hay, oats, rye, wheat, corn, sunflowers, tourism

History: In 1682 France claimed all the land drained by the Mississippi River system. This area included present-day South Dakota. The first known explorations of the region occurred in 1743. In 1803 the United States bought the territory in the Louisiana Purchase. Lewis and Clark followed the Missouri River through the region in 1804. In 1817 the French established the first permanent settlement. The Dakota Territory was created in 1861. In 1889 South Dakota became the fortieth state.

Historic sites and other attractions: Deadwood, Black Hills National Forest, Mount Rushmore National Memorial, Crazy Horse Memorial, Corn Palace, Badlands National Monument, Great Lakes of South Dakota, Jewel Cave National Monument

Unusual facts: South Dakota is a leading state in the amount of beef cattle, hogs, and lambs raised. The Homestake Mine leads in gold production in the United States. The geographic center of the 50 states is in South Dakota, about 17 miles (27 km) west of Castle Rock.

Original American Indian groups: Cheyenne, Dakota, Sutaio

TENNESSEE

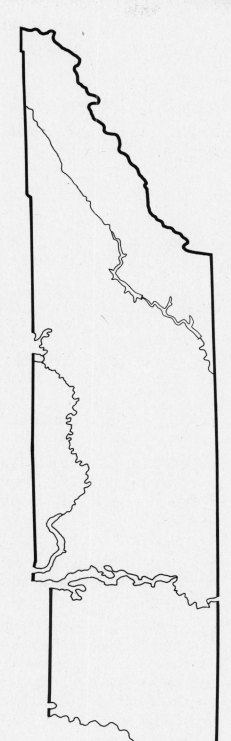

100 Miles

150 Kilometers

100

50

50

50

0

0

THE MAP BOOK

87

FACTS ABOUT
TENNESSEE

Population: 4,919,000

State flower: Iris

Capital: Nashville

State bird: Mockingbird

State nickname: The Volunteer State

Largest cities: Memphis, Nashville, Knoxville, Chattanooga, Clarksville

Major land areas: Appalachian Mountains, Appalachian Plateau, Blue Ridge Mountains, Gulf Coastal Plain, Interior Low Plateau, Mississippi Alluvial Plain

Lowest point: Along the Mississippi River in Shelby County, 182 feet (55 m) above sea level

Highest point: Clingmans Dome, 6,643 feet (2,025 m)

Major rivers: Cumberland River, Mississippi River, Tennessee River

Major bodies of water: Dale Hollow Lake, Kentucky Lake, Lake Barkley, Lake Chickamauga, Pickwick Lake, Watts Bar Lake (all artificial)

Climate: In January average temperatures range from 37°F (3°C) in the east to 40°F (4°C) in the west. In July average temperatures range from 71°F (22°C) in the east to 79°F (26°C) in the west. Most of the state averages 50 inches (130 cm) of precipitation a year.

Resources, industries, and products: Chemicals, transportation equipment, food products, electronics, machinery, clothing, cattle, hogs, soybeans, cotton

History: In 1540 Hernando de Soto explored the Tennessee region for Spain. In 1682 France claimed the Mississippi River valley. France later lost the area to the British in 1763, after the French and Indian War. In 1796 Tennessee became the sixteenth state.

Historic sites and other attractions: Andrew Johnson National Historic Site, Great Smoky Mountains National Park, American Museum of Science and Energy, Grand Ole Opry House, Shiloh National Military Park, The Hermitage, Lookout Mountain

Unusual facts: The Watauga Association drew up one of the first written constitutions in North America, in 1772. Tennessee was the last Confederate state to leave the Union and the first to be readmitted. More Civil War battles were fought in Tennessee than in any other state except Virginia. The Parthenon in Nashville is the world's only reproduction of the ancient Greek temple.

Original American Indian groups: Cherokee, Chickasaw, Kaskinampo, Shawnee

TEXAS

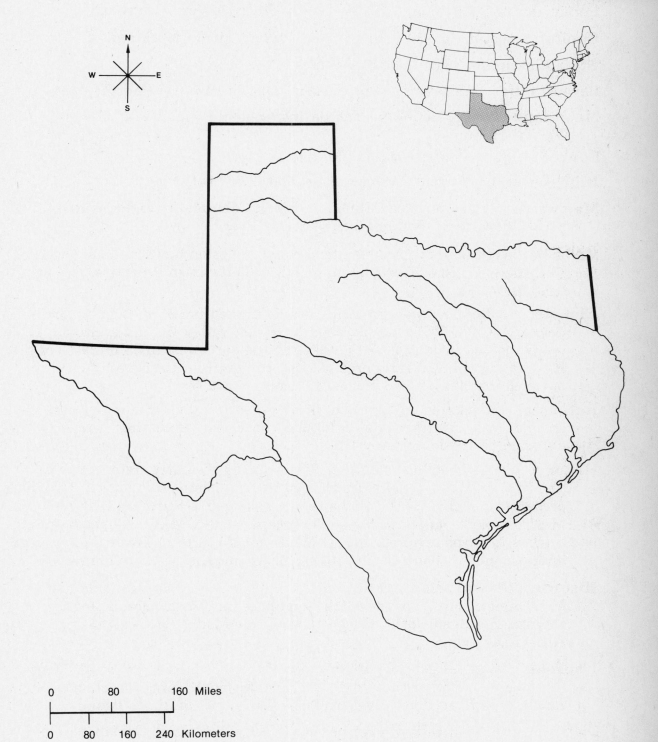

0   80   160   Miles

0   80   160   240   Kilometers

FACTS ABOUT
TEXAS

Population: 16,780,000

Capital: Austin

State flower: Bluebonnet

State bird: Mockingbird

State nickname: The Lone Star State

Largest cities: Houston, Dallas, San Antonio, El Paso, Fort Worth

Major land areas: Mountains and Basins, Central Plains, Great Plains, Coastal Plain

Lowest point: Along the Gulf of Mexico, sea level

Highest point: Guadalupe Peak, 8,751 feet (2,667 m)

Major rivers: Brazos River, Canadian River, Colorado River, Pecos River, Red River, Rio Grande, Sabine River, Trinity River

Major bodies of water: Amistad Reservoir, Galveston Bay, Gulf of Mexico, Lake Meredith, Lake Texoma (artificial), Sam Rayburn Reservoir, Toledo Bend Reservoir

Climate: In January average temperatures range from 35°F (2°C) in northwest Texas to 60°F (16°C) in the lower Rio Grande Valley. In July average temperatures range from 79°F (26°C) in the northwest to 85°F (29°C) in the Rio Grande Valley. Yearly precipitation ranges from 12 inches (30 cm) in parts of west Texas to 46 inches (117 cm) in east Texas.

Resources, industries, and products: Nonelectrical machinery, oil refining, chemical manufacturing, oil field machinery, food processing, petroleum and natural gas, cattle, cotton

History: Spanish explorers reached Texas during the early sixteenth century. The first settlements were established by Spanish missionaries in 1682 near present-day El Paso. Most of the region belonged to Spain until 1821, when Mexico broke from Spain and Texas became part of Mexico. American settlers in Texas revolted against Mexican rule in 1836. Texas then became an independent republic. In 1845 Texas became the twenty-eighth state.

Historic sites and other attractions: The Alamo, San Jacinto Monument, Mission San Jose, Lyndon B. Johnson Space Center, Lyndon B. Johnson Library, Big Bend National Park, Guadalupe Mountains National Park, Aquarena Springs

Unusual facts: Texas is one of the three states that have been independent countries. (The other two are Hawaii and Vermont.) King Ranch, a cattle ranch in Texas, is about the same size as the state of Rhode Island.

Original American Indian groups: Caddo, Coahuiltecan, Comanche, Karankawan, Lipan, Shuman, Tonkawan, Wichita

THE MAP BOOK

UTAH

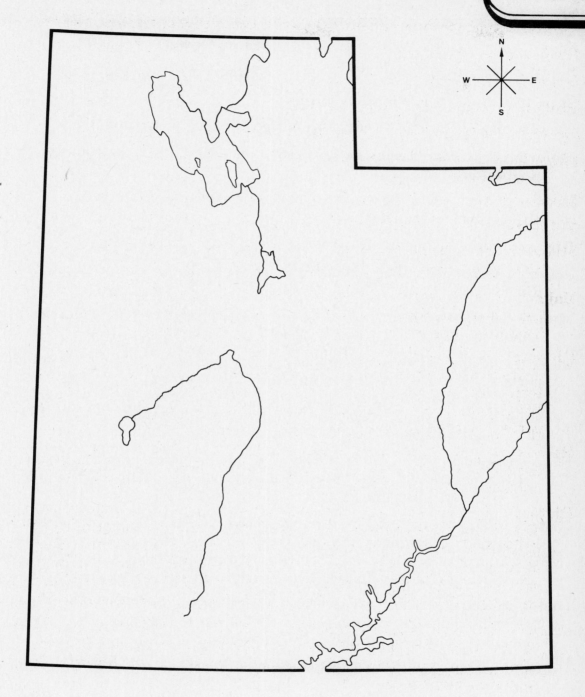

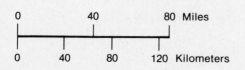

0   40   80 Miles

0   40   80 120 Kilometers

THE MAP BOOK

91

FACTS ABOUT
UTAH

Population: 1,691,000

Capital: Salt Lake City

State nickname: The Beehive State

State flower: Sego lily

State bird: Sea gull

Largest cities: Salt Lake City, Provo, Ogden, Orem, Bountiful

Major land areas: Basin and Range Region, Colorado Plateau, Rocky Mountains

Lowest point: Along Beaverdam Creek in Washington County, 2,000 feet (610 m) above sea level

Highest point: Kings Peak, 13,528 feet (4,123 m)

Major rivers: Bear River, Colorado River, Green River, Jordan River, Sevier River

Major bodies of water: Bear Lake, Flaming Gorge Reservoir, Great Salt Lake, Lake Powell (artificial), Sevier Lake, Utah Lake

Climate: In January average temperatures range from 20°F (-7°C) in the north to 39°F (4°C) in the southwest. In July average temperatures range from 60°F (16°C) in the north to 84°F (29°C) in the southwestern part of the state. Average yearly precipitation ranges from less than 5 inches (13 cm) in the Great Salt Lake Desert to 50 inches (130 cm) in the northeast.

Resources, industries, and products: Primary metals, guided missiles, tourism, electronics, machinery, food products, petroleum, copper, gold, iron ore, lead, uranium, cattle, milk, hay, wheat

History: Two Spanish explorers came to Utah in 1776. In 1847 Brigham Young led a group of Mormons into the Great Salt Lake region. One year later, the United States won possession of the territory from Mexico. In 1850 the Utah Territory was created. In 1896 Utah became the forty-fifth state.

Historic sites and other attractions: Mormon Tabernacle, Golden Spike National Historic Site, Zion National Park, Bryce Canyon National Park, Monument Valley, Great Salt Lake, Canyonlands National Park

Unusual facts: The Great Salt Lake is up to seven times saltier than any ocean in the world. It is also the largest natural lake west of the Mississippi. The first transcontinental railroad system was completed in Promontory, Utah, in 1869. The Mormon Tabernacle has one of the largest pipe organs in the world. Bingham Canyon Copper Pit is the largest open-pit copper mine in North America.

Original American Indian groups: Gosiute, Southern Paiute, Ute, Western Shoshoni

VERMONT

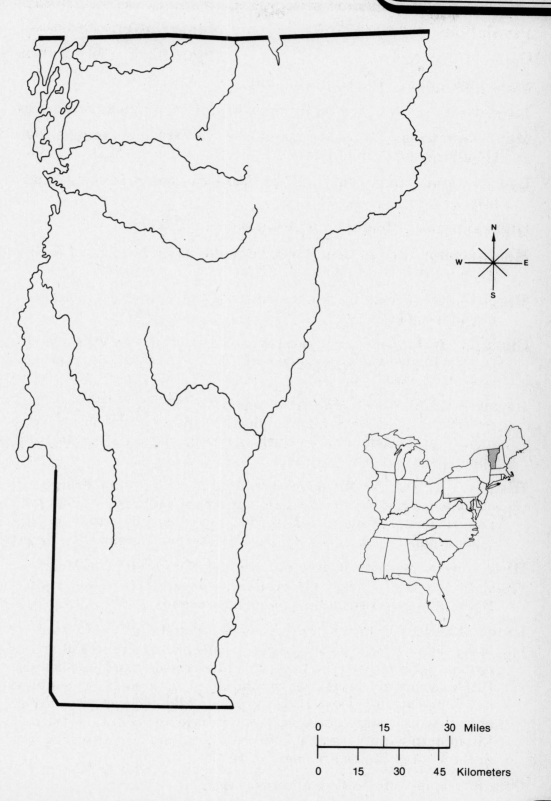

N
W · E
S

0	15	30 Miles

0	15	30	45	Kilometers

FACTS ABOUT
VERMONT

Population: 556,000

Capital: Montpelier

State flower: Red clover

State bird: Hermit thrush

State nickname: The Green Mountain State

Largest cities: Burlington, Rutland, Barre, Bennington, Brattleboro

Major land areas: Appalachian Mountains, Green Mountains, New England Upland, White Mountains

Lowest point: Lake Champlain in Franklin County, 95 feet (29 m) above sea level

Highest point: Mount Mansfield, 4,393 feet (1,339 m)

Major rivers: Connecticut River, Lamoille River, Missisquoi River, Otter Creek (river), White River, Winooski River

Major bodies of water: Bomoseen Lake, Lake Champlain, Lake Memphremagog

Climate: In January temperatures average 19°F (−7°C) throughout the state. In July temperatures average 68°F (20°C). Precipitation averages 40 inches (100 cm) a year.

Resources, industries, and products: Machine tools, electrical equipment, computer equipment, metal products, printing, paper and paper products, furniture, tourism, food products, granite, asbestos, marble, milk, potatoes, apples, maple syrup

History: In 1609 the Vermont region was claimed by the French. Massachusetts established the first permanent settlement there in 1724. Great Britain gained control of the region in 1763, but Vermont settlers created an independent republic in 1777. In 1791 Vermont became the fourteenth state.

Historic sites and other attractions: Bennington Battle Monument, Calvin Coolidge's birthplace, Old Constitution House, Green Mountain National Forest, Smuggler's Notch, Shelburne Museum

Unusual facts: Vermont has the smallest population of any state east of the Mississippi. It has the lowest percentage of city dwellers of any state in the nation. Vermont was the first state after the original 13 colonies to enter the Union. Many of the smaller communities in Vermont have a town meeting form of government in which the people take a direct part. Vermont is the only New England state that does not have an Atlantic coastline. Lake Champlain is the largest lake in New England. The largest granite quarries in the United States are near Barre.

Original American Indian groups: Abnaki, Mahican, Pennacook, Pocomtuc

VIRGINIA

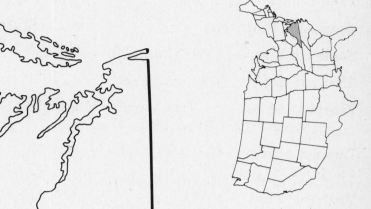

N E S W

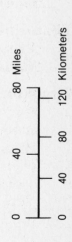

80 Miles

Kilometers

120

80

40

40

40

0

0

THE MAP BOOK

95

FACTS ABOUT
VIRGINIA

Population: 5,996,000

Capital: Richmond

State nickname: Old Dominion

State flower: Flowering dogwood

State bird: Cardinal

Largest cities: Virginia Beach, Norfolk, Richmond, Arlington, Newport News

Major land areas: Appalachian Mountains, Appalachian Plateau, Atlantic Coastal Plain, Blue Ridge Mountains, Piedmont

Lowest point: Along the Atlantic coast, sea level

Highest point: Mount Rogers, 5,729 feet (1,746 m)

Major rivers: James River, New River, Potomac River, Rappahannock River, Roanoke River, Shenandoah River, York River

Major bodies of water: Chesapeake Bay, Kerr Reservoir, Lake Anna, Lake Drummond, Smith Mountain Lake (artificial)

Climate: In January temperatures average 41°F (5°C) in the coastal region and 32°F (0°C) in parts of the Blue Ridge Mountains. In July temperatures average 78°F (26°C) on the coast and 68°F (20°C) in the mountains. Yearly precipitation averages 36 inches (91 cm) in the Shenandoah Valley and 44 inches (112 cm) in the southern part of the state.

Resources, industries, and products: Chemicals, boats and ships, shipbuilding, tourism, food products, coal, fishing, hogs, poultry, cattle, apples, corn, peanuts, soybeans

History: The first settlers in Virginia, who were Spanish, came in 1570. The first permanent settlement was established by the English in Jamestown in 1607. The Virginia Colony declared its independence from Great Britain in 1776. In 1788 Virginia became the tenth state.

Historic sites and other attractions: Skyline Drive, Virginia Beach, Arlington National Cemetery, Mount Vernon, Monticello, Williamsburg, Manassas National Battlefield Park, Appomattox Court House

Unusual facts: The College of William and Mary, founded in 1693, is the second-oldest college in the United States. The world's largest shipyard is in Newport News. Eight Presidents were born in Virginia: William Henry Harrison, Thomas Jefferson, James Madison, James Monroe, Zachary Taylor, John Tyler, George Washington, and Woodrow Wilson. More Civil War battles were fought in Virginia than in any other state.

Original American Indian groups: Cherokee, Manahoac, Meherrin, Monacan, Nahyssan, Nottaway, Occaneechi, Powhatan, Saponi, Shakori, Shawnee, Tutelo

WASHINGTON

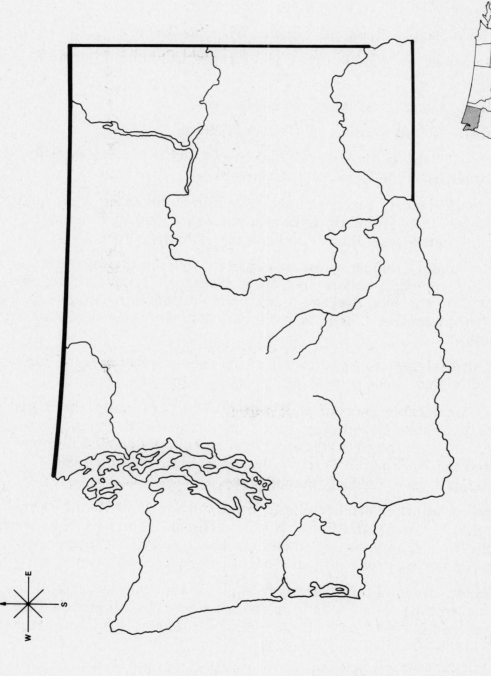

80 Miles

120 Kilometers

80

40

40

0

0

N
E
S
W

THE MAP BOOK

FACTS ABOUT
WASHINGTON

Population: 4,619,000

Capital: Olympia

State flower: Coast rhododendron

State bird: Willow goldfinch

State nickname: The Evergreen State

Largest cities: Seattle, Spokane, Tacoma, Bellevue, Everett

Major land areas: Cascade Range, Coast Ranges, Columbia Plateau, Rocky Mountains

Lowest point: Along the Pacific Ocean, sea level

Highest point: Mount Rainier, 14,410 feet (4,392 m)

Major rivers: Chehalis River, Columbia River, Cowlitz River, Skagit River, Snake River, Spokane River, Yakima River

Major bodies of water: Crescent Lake, Franklin D. Roosevelt Lake (artificial), Lake Chelan, Lake Quinault, Lake Sammamish, Lake Washington, Lake Whatcom, Ozette Lake, Puget Sound, Strait of Juan de Fuca

Climate: In January temperatures average 41°F (5°C) in the west and 25°F (−4°C) in the east. In July temperatures average 66°F (19°C) in the west and 70°F (21°C) in the east. Average yearly precipitation varies from 6 inches (15 cm) in the central plateau to 135 inches (343 cm) in parts of the Olympic Peninsula.

Resources, industries, and products: Airplanes, aerospace, ships, lumber and wood products, food processing, coal, fish, fruit, wheat

History: Spanish explorers claimed Washington in 1775. Later, the British also claimed the region. In 1805 Lewis and Clark reached the Pacific coast of Washington. The United States and Great Britain divided the territory in 1846, and the Washington Territory was created in 1853. In 1889 Washington became the forty-second state.

Historic sites and other attractions: Grand Coulee Dam, Mount Rainier National Park, Whitman Mission National Historic Site, Fort Vancouver National Historic Site, San Juan Islands, Lewis and Clark Interpretive Center, North Cascades National Park, Olympic National Park

Unusual facts: Washington grows more apples than any other state. It leads the nation in the production of hydroelectric power. Washington had the most snow recorded in North America for one winter. Mount St. Helens erupted on May 18, 1980.

Original American Indian groups: Chinook, Columbia, Colville, Kalispel, Klickitat, Nisqually, Okanagon, Sanpoil, Spokan, Wallawalla, Wishram, Yakima

WEST VIRGINIA

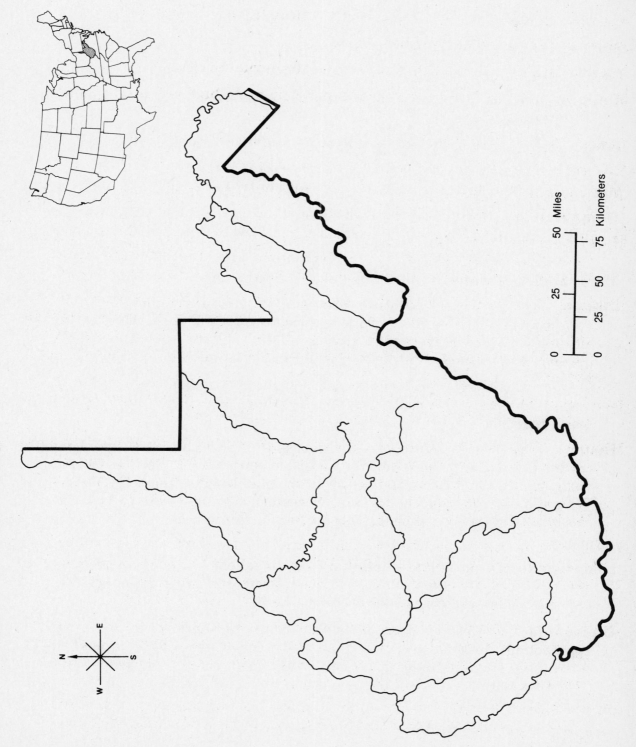

50 Miles

25

0

75 Kilometers

50

25

0

25

50

N E S W

FACTS ABOUT
WEST VIRGINIA

Population: 1,884,000

Capital: Charleston

State nickname: The Mountain State

State flower: Rhododendron

State bird: Cardinal

Largest cities: Charleston, Huntington, Wheeling, Parkersburg, Morgantown

Major land areas: Appalachian Mountains, Appalachian Plateau, Blue Ridge Mountains

Lowest point: Along the Potomac River in Jefferson County, 240 feet (73 m) above sea level

Highest point: Spruce Knob in Pendleton County, 4,862 feet (1,482 m)

Major rivers: Big Sandy River, Elk River, Guyandotte River, Kanawha River, Little Kanawha River, Monongahela River, New River, Ohio River, Potomac River, Shenandoah River

Major bodies of water: Bluestone Lake, E. Lynne Lake, Tygart Lake

Climate: In January temperatures average 33°F (1°C) throughout West Virginia, and in July the average temperature is 73°F (23°C) throughout the state. Precipitation averages 60 inches (152 cm) a year in the mountain regions and 35 inches (89 cm) a year in the northwest Panhandle.

Resources, industries, and products: Chemicals, timber, steel, nickel, limestone, sandstone, coal, natural gas, salt, cattle, chickens, milk, apples, corn, tourism

History: The West Virginia area was part of the Virginia Colony established by the English in 1606. The first European settlers were Germans seeking religious freedom. Later, the Scotch-Irish established settlements. When Virginia seceded from the Union, the western counties of the region formed a separate state government. In 1863 West Virginia became the thirty-fifth state.

Historic sites and other attractions: Monongahela National Forest, Harpers Ferry National Historical Park, Charles Town, Jackson's Mill, Berkeley Springs, Blennerhassett Island, Seneca Rock

Unusual facts: West Virginia ranks second only to Kentucky in coal production. Ice Mountain, near Racine, has ice at its base throughout the year. Cold air in its underground passages forms the ice and keeps it frozen. The first natural-gas well in the United States was discovered in West Virginia in 1815.

Original American Indian groups: Cherokee, Conoy, Delaware, Honniasont, Moneton, Shawnee, Susquehanna

WISCONSIN

N
W E
S

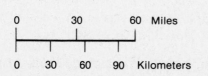

0   30   60   Miles

0   30   60   90   Kilometers

THE MAP BOOK

FACTS ABOUT
WISCONSIN

Population: 4,858,000

State flower: Wood violet

Capital: Madison

State bird: Robin

State nickname: The Badger State

Largest cities: Milwaukee, Madison, Green Bay, Racine, Kenosha

Major land areas: Central Plains, Superior Upland

Lowest point: Along the western shore of Lake Michigan, 581 feet (177 m) above sea level

Highest point: Timms Hill, 1,952 feet (595 m)

Major rivers: Black River, Chippewa River, Flambeau River, Menominee River, Mississippi River, St. Croix River, Wisconsin River

Major bodies of water: Green Bay, Green Lake, Lake Chippewa, Lake Michigan, Lake Superior, Lake Winnebago, Petenwell Lake

Climate: In January average temperatures range from 12°F (−11°C) in northwest Wisconsin to 22°F (−6°C) in the southeastern portion of the state. In July average temperatures range from 69°F (21°C) in the north to 73°F (23°C) in the south of the state. Yearly precipitation throughout Wisconsin averages 30 inches (76 cm).

Resources, industries, and products: Farm machinery, transportation equipment, electrical equipment, metal products, paper and wood products, lead, cattle, hogs, milk, butter, cheese, tourism

History: In 1634 French explorers landed on the shore of Green Bay. The French claimed this area and held it until 1763, when the British took control. In 1783, after the Revolutionary War, the United States won control of the region. Wisconsin Territory was established in 1836, and in 1848 Wisconsin became the thirtieth state.

Historic sites and other attractions: Wisconsin Dells, Apostle Islands, Ice Age National Scientific Reserve, Circus World Museum, Chequamegon National Forest, Nicolet National Forest

Unusual facts: Wisconsin alone produces about 40 percent of the nation's cheese. The first kindergarten, vocational school, and university correspondence course were all developed in Wisconsin. Wisconsin was the first state to pass a law requiring the use of safety belts in automobiles. The first hydroelectric plant in the nation was built on Fox River in 1882. The Ringling brothers started their first circus at Baraboo in 1884.

Original American Indian groups: Chippewa, Foxes, Kickapoo, Menominee, Sauk, Winnebago

WYOMING

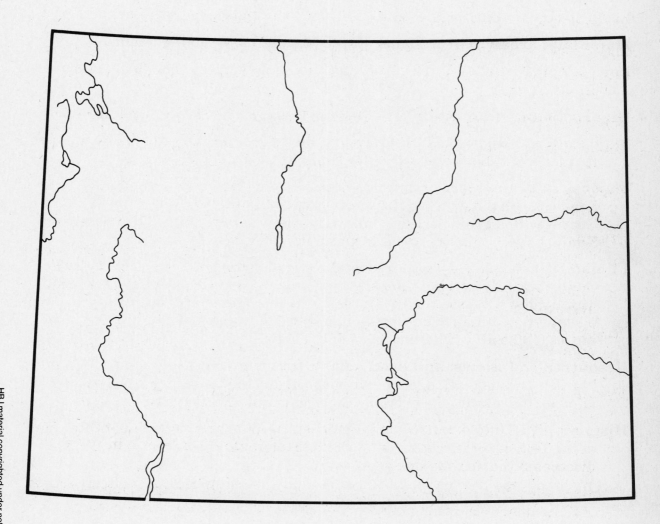

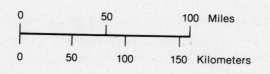

0   50   100 Miles

0   50   100   150 Kilometers

FACTS ABOUT
WYOMING

Population: 471,000

State flower: Indian paintbrush

Capital: Cheyenne

State bird: Meadowlark

State nickname: The Equality State

Largest cities: Casper, Cheyenne, Laramie, Rock Springs, Sheridan

Major land areas: Great Plains, Rocky Mountains, Wyoming Basin

Lowest point: Belle Fourche River in Crook County, 3,100 feet (945 m) above sea level

Highest point: Gannett Peak in Fremont County, 13,804 feet (4,207 m)

Major rivers: Bighorn River, Cheyenne River, Green River, North Platte River, Powder River, Snake River, Yellowstone River

Major bodies of water: Alcova Reservoir, Boysen Reservoir, Buffalo Bill Reservoir, Flaming Gorge Reservoir, Fremont Lake, Glendo Reservoir, Guernsey Reservoir, Jackson Lake, Keyhole Reservoir, Pathfinder Reservoir, Seminoe Reservoir, Shoshone Lake, Yellowstone Lake

Climate: In January average temperatures range from 12°F (−11°C) to 22°F (−6°C). In July average temperatures range from 59°F (15°C) to 71°F (22°C). Throughout the year, temperatures in the mountains are cooler than at lower elevations. Average yearly precipitation ranges from 5 inches (13 cm) to 50 inches (130 cm) in different parts of the state.

Resources, industries, and products: Petroleum and coal products, iron ore, tourism and recreation, clay and glass products, lumber and wood products, natural gas, uranium, sheep, cattle, sugar beets, wheat, hay

History: The United States bought most of the Wyoming region in 1803 as part of the Louisiana Purchase. John Colter explored the area in 1807 and discovered the Yellowstone geysers and hot springs. The territory of Wyoming was created in 1868, and in 1890 Wyoming became the forty-fourth state.

Historic sites and other attractions: Yellowstone National Park, Grand Teton National Park, Devils Tower National Monument, Fort Laramie National Historic Site, Fossil Butte National Monument, Wind River Canyon

Unusual facts: Wyoming Territory was the first place in the United States to grant women the right to vote. Because of Wyoming's history of equal rights for women, it is nicknamed The Equality State. Wyoming was the first state to elect a woman governor—Nellie Tayloe Ross was elected in 1924. Yellowstone, established in 1872, is the nation's oldest national park.

Original American Indian groups: Arapaho, Crow, Northern Shoshoni

THE UNITED STATES

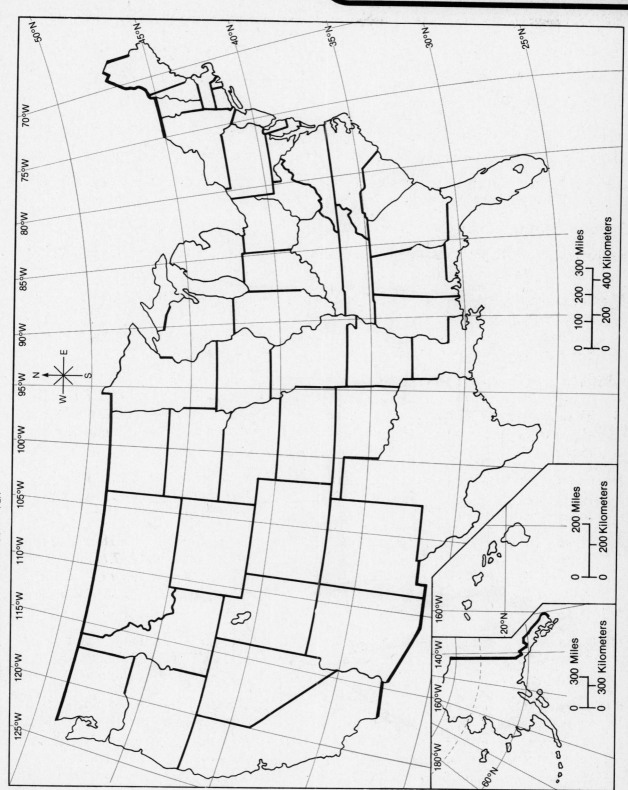

THE UNITED STATES

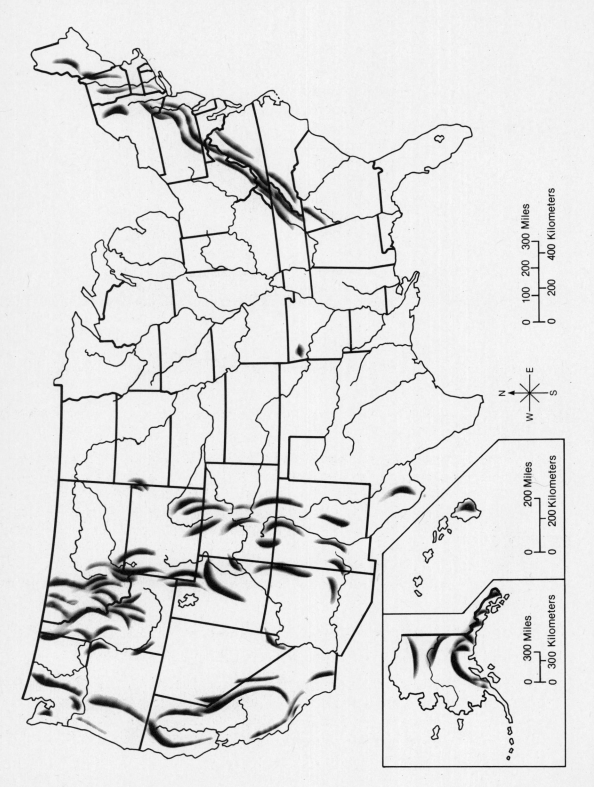

Miles
100 200 300 Miles
0 200 400 Kilometers

N
W —⦿— E
S

200 Miles
0 200 Kilometers

300 Miles
0 300 Kilometers

FACTS ABOUT
THE UNITED STATES

State population rank:

1 California	18 Maryland	35 West Virginia
2 New York	19 Washington	36 Utah
3 Texas	20 Louisiana	37 Nebraska
4 Florida	21 Minnesota	38 New Mexico
5 Pennsylvania	22 Alabama	39 Maine
6 Illinois	23 Kentucky	40 New Hampshire
7 Ohio	24 Arizona	41 Hawaii
8 Michigan	25 South Carolina	42 Nevada
9 New Jersey	26 Colorado	43 Idaho
10 North Carolina	27 Oklahoma	44 Rhode Island
11 Georgia	28 Connecticut	45 Montana
12 Virginia	29 Iowa	46 South Dakota
13 Massachusetts	30 Oregon	47 North Dakota
14 Indiana	31 Mississippi	48 Delaware
15 Missouri	32 Kansas	49 Vermont
16 Tennessee	33 Alaska	50 Wyoming
17 Wisconsin	34 Arkansas	

Total population (including Washington, D.C., and Puerto Rico):
237,480,000

Largest cities: New York City, Los Angeles, Chicago, Houston, Philadelphia, Detroit

Major land areas: Adirondack Mountains, Alaska Range, Appalachian Mountains, Appalachian Plateau, Arctic Plains, Atlantic Coastal Plain, Basin and Range Region, Blue Ridge Mountains, Brooks Range, Cascade Range, Central Lowlands and Uplands, Central Plains, Central Valley, Coast Ranges, Colorado Plateau, Columbia Plateau, Great Plains, Gulf Coastal Plain, Hawaii, Imperial Valley, Interior Low Plateau, Kahoolawe, Kauai, Lanai, Maui, Molokai, New England Upland, Niihau, Ouachita Mountains, Oahu, Ozark Plateau, Piedmont, Rocky Mountains, Sierra Nevada, Superior Upland, Wyoming Basin

Lowest point: Death Valley in California, 282 feet (86 m) below sea level

Highest point: Mount McKinley in Alaska, 20,320 feet (6,194 m)

Major rivers: Alabama River, Arkansas River, Brazos River, Colorado River, Columbia River, Connecticut River, Delaware River, Hudson River, James River, Mississippi River, Missouri River, Potomac River, Red River, Rio Grande, Sacramento River, San Joaquin River, Susquehanna River, Yukon River

Continued on page 108.

FACTS ABOUT
THE UNITED STATES

Major bodies of water: Chesapeake Bay, Delaware Bay, Great Salt Lake, Lake Erie, Lake Huron, Lake Iliamna, Lake Michigan, Lake of the Woods, Lake Okeechobee, Lake Ontario, Lake Superior, Lake Tahoe, Mobile Bay, Monterey Bay, Puget Sound

Climate: The United States has a broad range of climates, varying from the tropical climates of Hawaii and southern Florida to the subarctic climate of Alaska. The Southeast states have a subtropical climate with a lot of precipitation. The Northeast states have a mild climate with moderate precipitation. Farther west is the semiarid (steppe) climate of the Great Plains. The climate in the Southwest is arid. The hottest and driest places in the country are in the Southwest. On the Pacific coast, it is subtropical in southern California, and mild from northern California to southeastern Alaska. The Pacific Northwest is one of the wettest places in the country.

Resources, industries, and products: Aircraft, iron and steel products, machinery, metal products, paper and paper products, textiles, transportation equipment, aluminum, coal, copper, iron ore, lead, natural gas, oil, silver, zinc, cattle, hogs, sheep, dairy products, cotton, barley, wheat, corn, oats, fruit, soybeans, sugar, vegetables

History: Exploration began after Columbus sighted the Bahamas in 1492. The first Europeans to settle in what is now the United States were the Spanish. They built St. Augustine in Florida. English settlers started Jamestown in 1607. Soon many settlements began along the Atlantic coast. Most of these settlements were controlled by England. In the late 1700s Great Britain began asking for taxes that the Americans thought were unfair. This set off the American Revolution (1775–1783). The United States declared its independence on July 4, 1776. After the Revolution, United States citizens adopted the Constitution and elected George Washington as their first President. The country began to grow westward. In 1783 our western border was the Mississippi River. By 1850 the western border was the Pacific Ocean. The new states forming in the West had many links to the North. Southern leaders were afraid to lose power in the government. When Abraham Lincoln was elected President, the South withdrew from the Union. Civil War broke out in 1861. The war ended in 1865, and the United States remained one nation. Russia sold Alaska to the United States for more than $7 million in 1867. In 1959 Hawaii became the fiftieth state.

Major explorers: Sebastian Cabot, Ponce de León, Francisco de Coronado, Giovanni da Verrazano, Jacques Cartier, Hernando de Soto, Francis Drake, Samuel de Champlain, John Smith, Henry Hudson, Jacques Marquette, Louis Joliet, Robert de La Salle, James Cook, Meriwether Lewis and William Clark, Zebulon Pike, John Fremont, John W. Powell

STATE ABBREVIATIONS AND POSTAL ABBREVIATIONS

Alabama: Ala., AL

Alaska: Alaska, AK

Arizona: Ariz., AZ

Arkansas: Ark., AR

California: Calif., CA

Colorado: Colo., CO

Connecticut: Conn., CT

Delaware: Del., DE

Florida: Fla., FL

Georgia: Ga., GA

Hawaii: Hawaii, HI

Idaho: Idaho, ID

Illinois: Ill., IL

Indiana: Ind., IN

Iowa: Iowa, IA

Kansas: Kans., KS

Kentucky: Ky., KY

Louisiana: La., LA

Maine: Maine, ME

Maryland: Md., MD

Massachusetts: Mass., MA

Michigan: Mich., MI

Minnesota: Minn., MN

Mississippi: Miss., MS

Missouri: Mo., MO

Montana: Mont., MT

Nebraska: Nebr., NE

Nevada: Nev., NV

New Hampshire: N.H., NH

New Jersey: N.J., NJ

New Mexico: N.Mex., NM

New York: N.Y., NY

North Carolina: N.C., NC

North Dakota: N.Dak., ND

Ohio: Ohio, OH

Oklahoma: Okla., OK

Oregon: Oreg., OR

Pennsylvania: Pa., PA

Rhode Island: R.I., RI

South Carolina: S.C., SC

South Dakota: S. Dak., SD

Tennessee: Tenn., TN

Texas: Tex., TX

Utah: Utah, UT

Vermont: Vt., VT

Virginia: Va., VA

Washington: Wash., WA

West Virginia: W.Va., WV

Wisconsin: Wis., WI

Wyoming: Wyo., WY

FOR MAKING GRAPHS

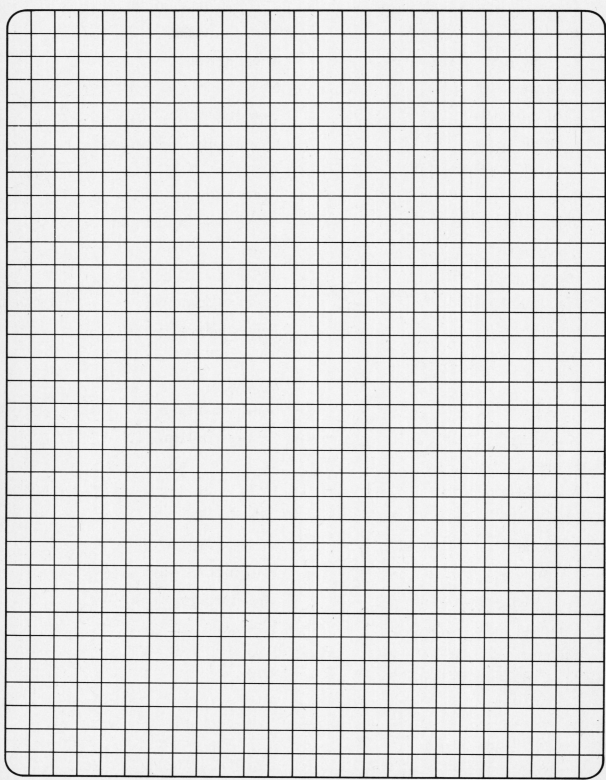

THE MAP BOOK

UNITED STATES REGIONS

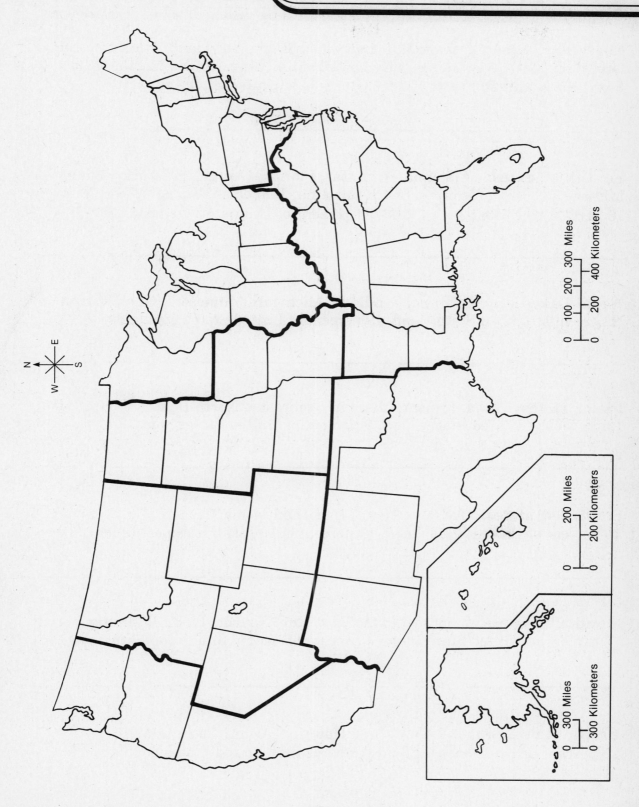

N E
W S

300 Miles
400 Kilometers
0 100 200 300
0 200

200 Miles
200 Kilometers
0
0

300 Miles
300 Kilometers
0
0

FACTS ABOUT
UNITED STATES REGIONS

Northeast states: Connecticut, Delaware, Maine, Maryland, Massachusetts, New Hampshire, New Jersey, New York, Pennsylvania, Rhode Island, Vermont
5 percent of United States land, 23 percent of United States population

Southeast states: Alabama, Arkansas, Florida, Georgia, Kentucky, Louisiana, Mississippi, North Carolina, South Carolina, Tennessee, Virginia, West Virginia
15 percent of United States land, 24 percent of United States population

Great Lakes states: Illinois, Indiana, Michigan, Minnesota, Ohio, Wisconsin
9 percent of United States land, 19 percent of United States population

Plains states: Iowa, Kansas, Missouri, Nebraska, North Dakota, South Dakota
12 percent of United States land, 5 percent of United States population

Southwest states: Arizona, New Mexico, Oklahoma, Texas
16 percent of United States land, 10 percent of United States population

Mountain states: Colorado, Idaho, Montana, Nevada, Utah, Wyoming
17 percent of United States land, 3 percent of United States population

Pacific states: Alaska, California, Hawaii, Oregon, Washington
25 percent of United States land, 16 percent of United States population

THE NORTHEAST

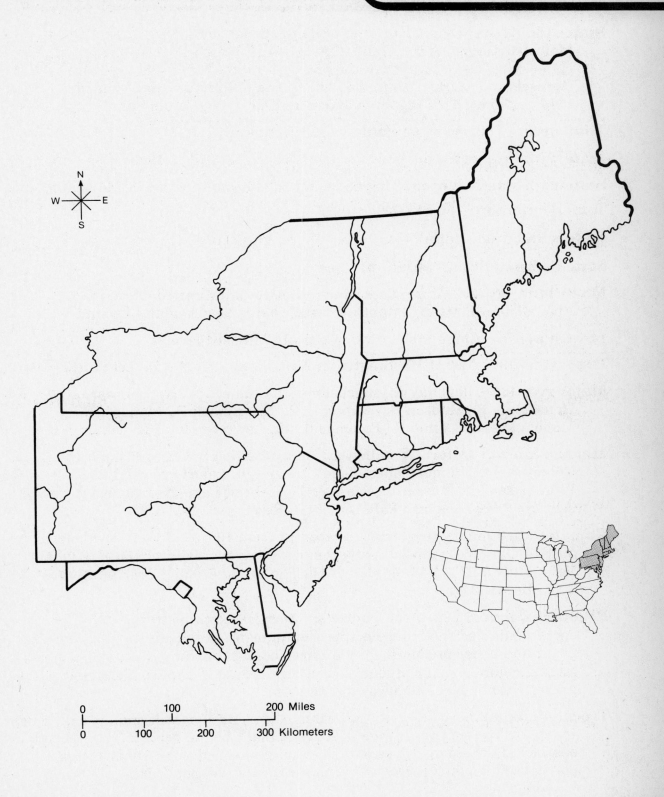

0   100   200 Miles

0   100   200   300 Kilometers

FACTS ABOUT
THE NORTHEAST

States (and ✪capital cities): Connecticut (✪Hartford), Delaware (✪Dover), Maine (✪Augusta), Maryland (✪Annapolis), Massachusetts (✪Boston), New Hampshire (✪Concord), New Jersey (✪Trenton), New York (✪Albany), Pennsylvania (✪Harrisburg), Rhode Island (✪Providence), Vermont (✪Montpelier). This region includes the District of Columbia.

Total area: 182,054 square miles (471,519 sq km)

State with largest area: New York, 49,576 square miles (128,401 sq km)

State with smallest area: Rhode Island, 1,214 square miles (3,144 sq km)

Total population: 56,541,000

State with largest population: New York, 17,898,000

State with smallest population: Vermont, 556,000

Major land areas: Adirondack Mountains, Appalachian Mountains, Appalachian Plateau, Atlantic Coastal Plain, New England Upland

Lowest point: Along the Atlantic Coastal Plain, sea level

Highest point: Mount Washington in New Hampshire, 6,288 feet (1,917 m)

Major rivers: Allegheny R., Blackstone R., Connecticut R., Delaware R., Housatonic R., Hudson R., Kennebec R., Merrimack R., Mohawk R., Monongahela R., Ohio R., Potomac R., St. Lawrence R., Susquehanna R.

Major bodies of water: Candlewood Lake (artificial), Chesapeake Bay, Delaware Bay, Finger Lakes, Lake Champlain, Lake Ontario, Lake Winnipesaukee, Massachusetts Bay, Moosehead Lake, Narragansett Bay, New York Bay, Niagara Falls, Quabbin Reservoir

Climate: In January temperatures average from 19°F (−7°C) in Vermont to 39°F (4°C) in Maryland. In July temperatures average from 68°F (20°C) in Vermont to 75°F (24°C) in Maryland. The average yearly precipitation is 40 inches (102 cm).

Resources, industries, and products: Textiles, clothing, transportation equipment, electrical and electronic equipment, chemicals, processed foods, paper and paper products, shipbuilding, book publishing, coal, iron ore, oil, fishing, poultry, dairy products, corn, hay, potatoes, apples, blueberries, grapes, cranberries, maple syrup, tourism

Trees and animals: *Trees*—beech, birch, cedar, fir, hemlock, maple, oak, pine, spruce, tulip tree *Animals*—beavers, black bears, bobcats, copperheads, deer, foxes, lobsters, lynxes, minks, moose, muskrats, opossums, otters, porcupines, rabbits, raccoons, skunks, squirrels, woodchucks

THE SOUTHEAST

N
W—E
S

0   100   200 Miles

0   100   200   300 Kilometers

FACTS ABOUT
THE SOUTHEAST

States (and ✪capital cities): Alabama (✪Montgomery), Arkansas (✪Little Rock), Florida (✪Tallahassee), Georgia (✪Atlanta), Kentucky (✪Frankfort), Louisiana (✪Baton Rouge), Mississippi (✪Jackson), North Carolina (✪Raleigh), South Carolina (✪Columbia), Tennessee (✪Nashville), Virginia (✪Richmond), West Virginia (✪Charleston)

Total area: 533,091 square miles (1,432,505 sq km)

State with largest area: Georgia, 58,876 square miles (152,488 sq km)

State with smallest area: South Carolina, 31,055 square miles (80,432 sq km)

Total population: 58,821,000

State with largest population: Florida, 12,377,000

State with smallest population: West Virginia, 1,844,000

Major land areas: Appalachian Mountains, Appalachian Plateau, Atlantic Coastal Plain, Blue Ridge Mountains, Gulf Coastal Plain, Interior Low Plateau, Ouachita Mountains, Ozark Plateau, Piedmont

Lowest point: New Orleans, Louisiana, 5 feet (1.5 m) below sea level

Highest point: Mount Mitchell in North Carolina, 6,684 feet (2,037 m)

Major rivers: Alabama R., Altamaha R., Arkansas R., Chattahoochee R., Flint R., Kentucky R., Mississippi R., Mobile R., Ohio R., Pearl R., Potomac R., Red R., Roanoke R., Sabine R., Savannah R., Tennessee R., Tombigbee R.

Major bodies of water: Albemarle Sound, Chesapeake Bay, Guntersville Lake (artificial), Kentucky Lake (artificial), Kerr Reservoir, Lake Cumberland, Lake Okeechobee, Lake Ouachita, Lake Pontchartrain, Lake Seminole, Mobile Bay, Pamlico Sound, Roanoke Rapids (artificial)

Climate: In January temperatures average from 33°F (1°C) in West Virginia to 67°F (19°C) in Florida. In July temperatures average 83°F (28°C) in Florida and become cooler as you travel north. The average yearly precipitation is 46 inches (117 cm), but there can be up to 100 inches (250 cm) in some areas.

Resources, industries, and products: Textiles, chemicals, paper products, furniture, processed foods, electrical equipment, shipbuilding, coal, iron, oil, natural gas, lumber, fishing, cattle, hogs, poultry, dairy products, cotton, soybeans, peanuts, corn, rice, apples, oranges, sugarcane, tomatoes, tourism

Trees and animals: *Trees*—ash, bald cyprus, bay, beech, fir, gum, hickory, maple, oak, pine, spruce, tulip tree *Animals*—alligators, bears, beavers, bobcats, deer, Florida panthers, foxes, minks, muskrats, opossums, rabbits, raccoons, skunks, squirrels, weasels, wild hogs, wild turkeys, woodchucks

THE GREAT LAKES STATES

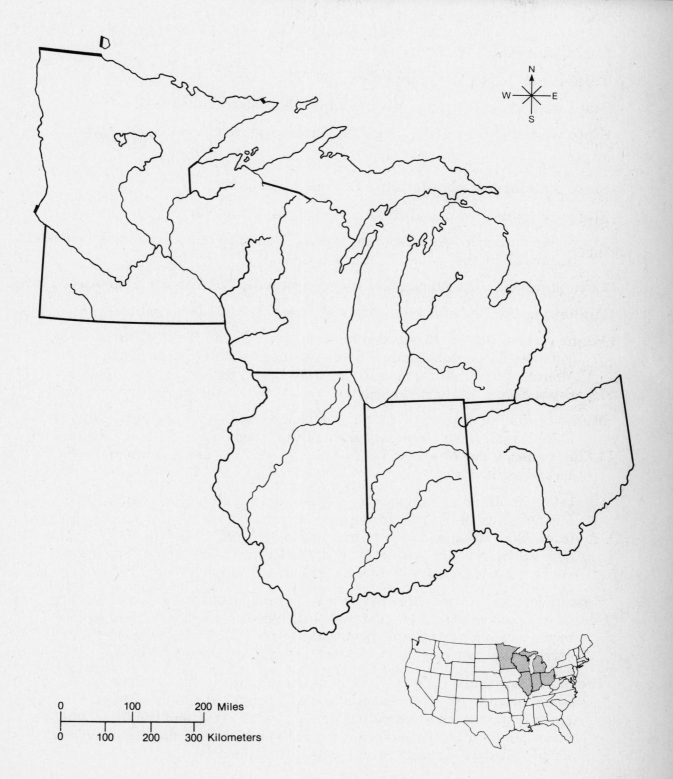

0		100		200 Miles

0	100	200	300 Kilometers

THE MAP BOOK

FACTS ABOUT
THE GREAT LAKES STATES

States (and ✪capital cities):   Illinois (✪Springfield), Indiana (✪Indianapolis), Michigan (✪Lansing), Minnesota (✪St. Paul), Ohio (✪Columbus), Wisconsin (✪Madison)

Total area: 332,351 square miles (860,789 sq km)

State with largest area: Minnesota, 84,068 square miles (217,035 sq km)

State with smallest area: Indiana, 36,291 square miles (93,993 sq km)

Total population: 46,455,000

State with largest population: Illinois, 11,544,000

State with smallest population: Minnesota, 4,306,000

Major land areas: Appalachian Plateau, Central Plains, Interior Low Plateau, Superior Upland

Lowest point: The Mississippi River in Illinois, 279 feet (85 m) above sea level

Highest point: Eagle Mountain in Minnesota, 2,301 feet (701 m)

Major rivers: Black River, Des Moines River, Grand River, Illinois River, Maumee River, Menominee River, Minnesota River, Mississippi River, Montreal River, Muskegon River, Ohio River, Red River of the North, St. Croix River, Scioto River, Wabash River, White River, Wisconsin River

Major bodies of water: Green Lake, Houghton Lake, Lake Erie, Lake Huron, Lake Itasca, Lake Michigan, Lake of the Woods, Lake St. Clair, Lake Superior, Lake Wawasee, Leech Lake, Mille Lacs Lake, Minnehaha Falls, Red Lake, Saginaw Bay

Climate: In January temperatures average from 2°F (−17°C) in upper Minnesota to 36°F (2°C) in southern Illinois. In July temperatures average from 68°F (20°C) in upper Minnesota to 79°F (26°C) in Illinois. The climate gets warmer as you travel south in the Great Lakes region. The average yearly precipitation is 33 inches (84 cm).

Resources, industries, and products: Transportation equipment, machinery, metals, processed foods, meat packing, electronic equipment, chemicals, paper and paper products, book publishing, coal, iron ore, copper, oil, fishing, cattle, hogs, poultry, dairy products, corn, hay, wheat, soybeans, oats, tourism

Trees and animals: *Trees*—aspen, basswood, beech, fir, hemlock, hickory, larch, maple, oak, pine, spruce, yellow birch   *Animals*—badgers, beavers, black bears, bobcats, Canadian geese, coyotes, gray and red foxes, gophers, moose, muskrats, opossums, otters, prairie mice, rabbits, raccoons, squirrels, striped skunks, weasels, white-tailed deer, woodchucks

THE PLAINS STATES

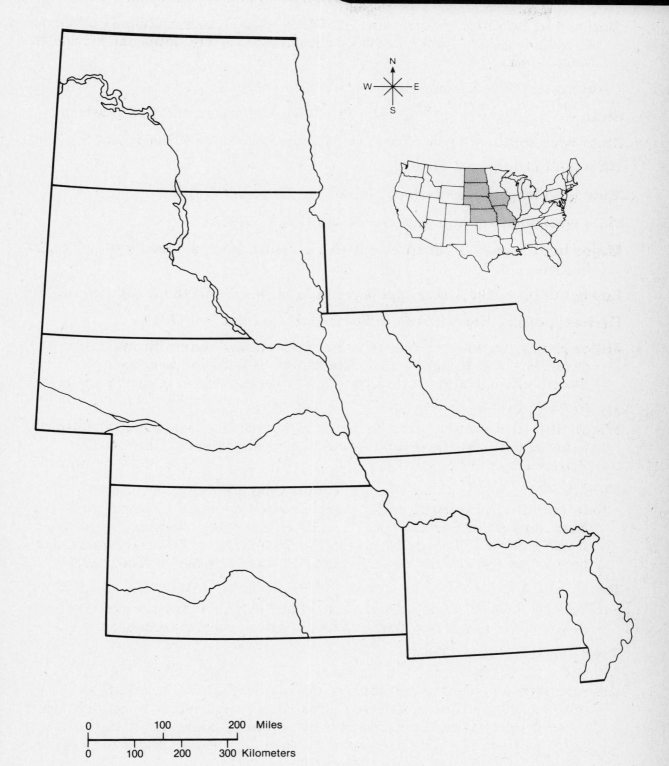

N
W — E
S

0   100   200 Miles

0   100   200   300 Kilometers

FACTS ABOUT
THE PLAINS STATES

States (and ✪capital cities):   Iowa (✪Des Moines), Kansas (✪Topeka), Missouri (✪Jefferson City), Nebraska (✪Lincoln), North Dakota (✪Bismarck), South Dakota (✪Pierre)

Total area: 433,179 square miles (1,121,934 sq km)

State with largest area: Kansas, 82,264 square miles (312,063 sq km)

State with smallest area: Iowa, 56,290 square miles (145,790 sq km)

Total population: 13,439,000

State with largest population: Missouri, 5,139,000

State with smallest population: North Dakota, 663,000

Major land areas: Central Plains, Great Plains, Interior Low Plateau, Ozark Plateau

Lowest point: The Mississippi River in Iowa, 480 feet (146 m) above sea level

Highest point: Harney Peak in South Dakota, 7,242 feet (2,207 m)

Major rivers: Arkansas River, Big Sioux River, Des Moines River, Mississippi River, Missouri River, North Platte River, Platte River, Red River, St. Francis River, South Platte River, Yellowstone River

Major bodies of water: Clear Lake, Devils Lake, Lake Francis Case (artificial), Lake McConaughy (artificial), Lake Oahe (artificial), Lake of the Ozarks (artificial), Lake Sakakawea (artificial), Milford Lake (artificial), Wappapello Reservoir

Climate: In January temperatures average from 3°F (−16°C) in North Dakota to 32°F (0°C) in Kansas. In July temperatures average from 69°F (21°C) in North Dakota to 79°F (26°C) in Kansas. The average yearly precipitation in North Dakota and South Dakota is 18 inches (46 cm). The average yearly precipitation in the rest of the Plains states is 34 inches (86 cm).

Resources, industries, and products: Transportation equipment, chemicals, book publishing, machinery, meat packing, food processing, metals, oil, coal, gold, cattle, pigs, sheep, dairy products, wheat, corn, soybeans, oats, tourism

Trees and animals: *Trees*—aspen, cottonwood, hickory, oak, pine, willow *Animals*—badgers, beavers, bighorn sheep, bobcats, buffaloes, cottontail rabbits, coyotes, elks, flickertail ground squirrels, foxes, jack rabbits, lynxes, mule deer, muskrats, opossums, prairie dogs, pronghorn antelopes, rabbits, raccoons, skunks, squirrels, weasels, white-tailed deer

THE SOUTHWEST

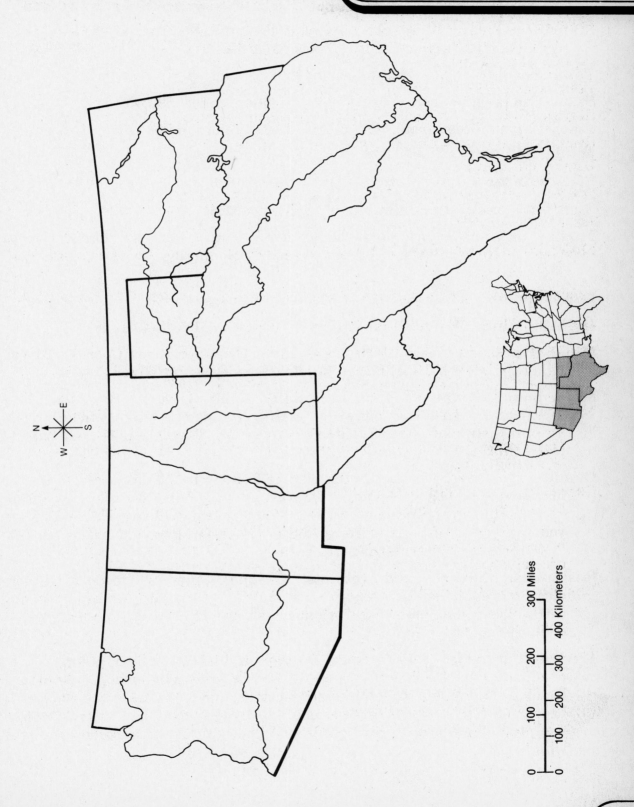

N
W E
S

300 Miles
400 Kilometers

0   100   200   300
0   100   200   300   400

FACTS ABOUT
THE SOUTHWEST

States (and ✪capital cities): Arizona (✪Phoenix), New Mexico (✪Santa Fe), Oklahoma (✪Oklahoma City), Texas (✪Austin)

Total area: 572,832 square miles (1,483,635 sq km)

State with largest area: Texas, 267,338 square miles (692,402 sq km)

State with smallest area: Oklahoma, 69,919 square miles (181,089 sq km)

Total population: 25,019,000

State with largest population: Texas, 16,780,000

State with smallest population: New Mexico, 1,510,000

Major land areas: Basin and Range Region, Central Plains, Colorado Plateau, Great Plains, Gulf Coastal Plain, Ouachita Mountains, Ozark Plateau, Rocky Mountains

Lowest point: Along the Gulf of Mexico in Texas, sea level

Highest point: Wheeler Peak in New Mexico, 13,161 feet (4,011 m)

Major rivers: Arkansas River, Brazos River, Canadian River, Colorado River, Gila River, Pecos River, Red River, Rio Grande, Sabine River

Major bodies of water: Elephant Butte Reservoir, Galveston Bay, Lake Mead (artificial), Lake O'The Cherokees (artificial), Lake Powell (artificial), Lake Texoma (artificial), San Carlos Lake (artificial), Theodore Roosevelt Lake (artificial)

Climate: In January temperatures average from 35°F (2°C) in northern New Mexico to 60°F (16°C) in southern Texas. In July temperatures average from 74°F (23°C) in New Mexico to 85°F (29°C) in southern Texas. The average yearly precipitation varies from 7 inches (18 cm) in Phoenix, Arizona, to 48 inches (122 cm) in Houston, Texas.

Resources, industries, and products: Chemicals, processed foods, machinery, electronic equipment, metals, oil, coal, natural gas, copper, uranium, fishing, cattle, sheep, dairy products, cotton, wheat, hay, rice, carrots, onions, spinach, melons, tourism

Trees and animals: *Trees*—aspen, Douglas fir, hickory, juniper, pinon, ponderosa pine, scrub oak, spruce *Shrubs*—creosote bush, greasewood, lechuquilla, sagebrush, sotol, saguaro cactus, yucca *Animals*—badgers, beavers, black bears, bobcats, chipmunks, coyotes, foxes, jack rabbits, minks, mountain lions, otters, prairie dogs, pronghorn antelopes, raccoons, squirrels, white-tailed deer

THE MOUNTAIN STATES

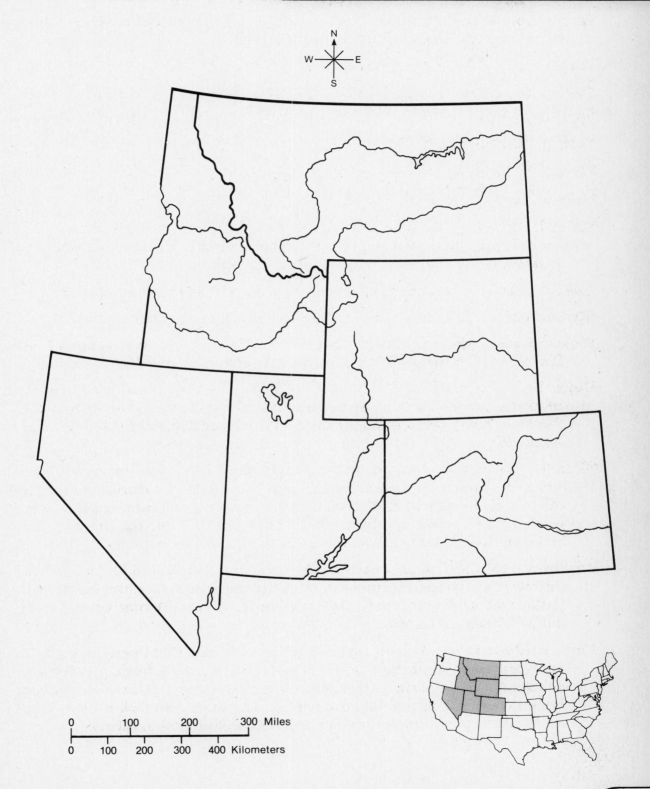

0   100   200   300 Miles

0   100   200   300   400 Kilometers

FACTS ABOUT
THE MOUNTAIN STATES

States (and ✪capital cities): Colorado (✪Denver), Idaho (✪Boise), Montana (✪Helena), Nevada (✪Carson City), Utah (✪Salt Lake City), Wyoming (✪Cheyenne)

Total area: 628,312 square miles (1,627,328 sq km)

State with largest area: Montana, 147,138 square miles (381,086 sq km)

State with smallest area: Idaho, 83,557 square miles (216,412 sq km)

Total population: 8,315,000

State with largest population: Colorado, 3,290,000

State with smallest population: Wyoming, 471,000

Major land areas: Basin and Range Region, Colorado Plateau, Columbia Plateau, Great Plains, Rocky Mountains, Wyoming Basin

Lowest point: The Colorado River in Nevada, 470 feet (143 m) above sea level

Highest point: Mount Elbert in Colorado, 14,433 feet (4,399 m)

Major rivers: Arkansas River, Bighorn River, Colorado River, Columbia River, Green River, Missouri River, North Platte River, Powder River, Salmon River, Snake River, South Platte River, Yellowstone River

Major bodies of water: Coeur d'Alene Lake, Flaming Gorge Reservoir, Flathead Lake, Fort Peck Lake (artificial), Great Salt Lake, Lake Mead (artificial), Lake Powell (artificial), Lake Tahoe, Pend Oreille Lake, Yellowstone Lake

Climate: In January temperatures average from 10°F (−12°C) in the northern mountain areas to 43°F (6°C) in Nevada. In July temperatures average from 60°F (16°C) in north Montana to 86°F (30°C) in Nevada. The average yearly precipitation ranges from 7 inches (18 cm) in Nevada to 50 inches (130 cm) in the northern Rockies.

Resources, industries, and products: Processed foods, lumber and wood products, lead, zinc, copper, silver, gold, coal, oil, natural gas, cattle, sheep, dairy products, hay, wheat, corn, barley, sugar beets, potatoes, tourism

Trees and animals: *Trees*—aspen, cottonwood, Douglas fir, hemlock, juniper, larch, pine, spruce, willow *Shrubs*—cacti, ocotillo, palo verde, sagebrush, shadscale *Animals*—badgers, bears, bobcats, cougars, coyotes, elks, foxes, lynxes, martens, moose, mountain goats, mountain lions, mule deer, muskrats, prairie dogs, pronghorn antelopes, Rocky Mountain sheep

THE PACIFIC STATES

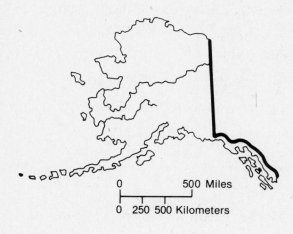

500 Miles

0   250 500 Kilometers

N

W — E

S

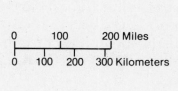

0   100   200 Miles

0   100   200   300 Kilometers

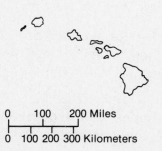

0   100   200 Miles

0   100 200 300 Kilometers

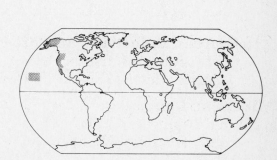

THE MAP BOOK

FACTS ABOUT
THE PACIFIC STATES

States (and ⊙capital cities): Alaska (⊙Juneau), California (⊙Sacramento), Hawaii (⊙Honolulu), Oregon (⊙Salem), Washington (⊙Olympia)

Total area: 920,073 square miles (2,382,989 sq km)

State with largest area: Alaska, 589,757 square miles (1,527,464 sq km)

State with smallest area: Hawaii, 6,450 square miles (16,705 sq km)

Total population: 39,043,000

State with largest population: California, 28,168,000

State with smallest population: Hawaii 1,093,000

Major land areas: Alaska Range, Arctic Plains, Basin and Range Region, Brooks Range, Cascade Range, Central Lowlands and Uplands, Central Valley, Coast Ranges, Columbia Plateau, Imperial Valley, Rocky Mountains, Sierra Nevada

Lowest point: Death Valley in California, 282 feet (86 m) below sea level

Highest point: Mount McKinley in Alaska, 20,320 feet (6,194 m)

Major rivers: Columbia River, Kuskokwim River, Sacramento River, San Joaquin River, Willamette River, Yukon River

Major bodies of water: Crater Lake, Iliamna Lake, Lake Tahoe, Monterey Bay, Pearl Harbor, Puget Sound, Salton Sea, San Francisco Bay, Shasta Lake

Climate: In January temperatures average from 25°F (−4°C) in Washington to 55°F (13°C) in California. In July temperatures average from 70°F (21°C) in Washington to 73°F (23°C) in California. The average yearly precipitation ranges from 10 inches (25 cm) in California to as much as 135 inches (343 cm) in Washington. In Alaska, January temperatures average from −11°F (−24°C) in the Arctic to 28°F (−2°C) in the south. Alaska's July temperatures average from 47°F (8°C) to 55°F (13°C). Alaska's yearly precipitation varies from 4 inches (10 cm) to 20 inches (51 cm). In Hawaii, temperatures average 71°F (22°C) in January and 77°F (21°C) in July. Hawaii's yearly precipitation varies from 10 inches (25 cm) to 300 inches (760 cm).

Resources, industries, and products: Paper products, jet airplanes, film production, oil, fishing, cattle, dairy products, hay, wheat, vegetables, cherries, apples, berries, pineapples, sugarcane, coffee, tourism

Trees and animals: *Trees*—Douglas fir, hemlock, juniper, koa, larch, oak, palm, pine, redwood, spruce *Animals*—antelopes, bears, deer, dolphins, elks, foxes, minks, mountain goats, musk oxen, seals, wildcats, wolverines

THE MIDDLE EAST

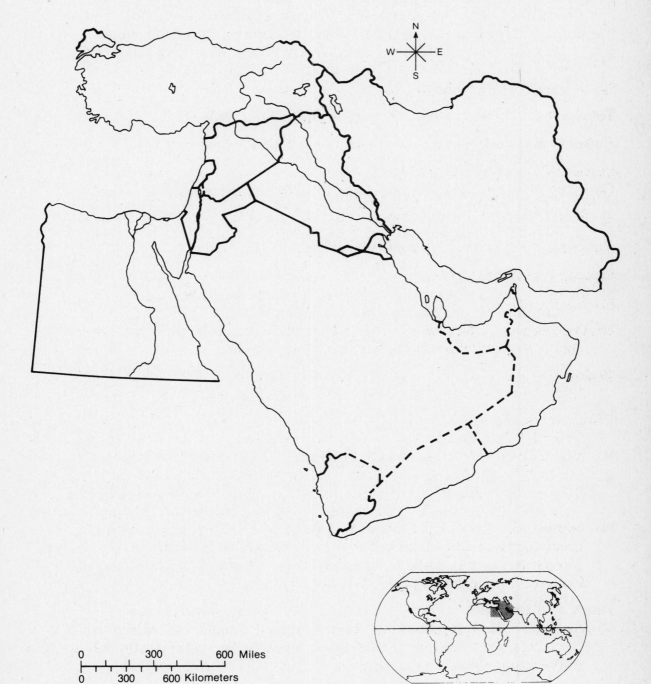

0   300   600   Miles

0   300   600   Kilometers

THE MAP BOOK

FACTS ABOUT
THE MIDDLE EAST

Countries (and ✪capital cities):   Bahrain (✪Manama), Cyprus (✪Nicosia), Egypt (✪Cairo), Iran (✪Tehran), Iraq (✪Baghdad), Israel (✪Jerusalem), Jordan (✪Amman), Kuwait (✪Kuwait), Lebanon (✪Beirut), Oman (✪Muscat), Qatar (✪Doha), Saudi Arabia (✪Riyadh), Syria (✪Damascus), Turkey (✪Ankara), United Arab Emirates (✪Abu Dhabi), Yemen (✪Sana), Yemen (P.D.R.) (✪Aden)

Total area: 2,850,737 square miles (7,372,577 sq km)

Country with largest area: Saudi Arabia, 864,869 square miles (2,240,000 sq km)

Country with smallest area: Bahrain, 261 square miles (677 sq km)

Total population: 229,776,000

Country with largest population: Turkey, 55,377,000

Country with smallest population: Qatar, 342,000

Major land areas: Anatolian Plateau, Arabian Peninsula, Caucasus Mountains, Elburz Mountains, Gilf Kebir Plateau, Great Kavir, Jordan-Dead Sea-Bekka Valley Lowland, Lebanon Mountains, Nile Valley, Oman Mountains, Plateau of Iran, Pontic Mountains, Qattara Depression, Sinai Peninsula, Taurus Mountains, Tigris-Euphrates Lowland, Zagros Mountains

Lowest point: Dead Sea in Israel and Jordan, 1,312 feet (399 m) below sea level

Highest point: Mount Damavand in Turkey, 18,610 feet (5,670 m)

Major rivers: Euphrates River, Jordan River, Karun River, Nile River, Shatt al Arab, Tigris River

Major bodies of water: Aegean Sea, Arabian Sea, Black Sea, Caspian Sea, Dead Sea, Gulf of Aden, Gulf of Aqaba, Gulf of Oman, Gulf of Suez, Lake Nasser (artificial), Lake Urmia, Lake Van, Persian Gulf, Red Sea, Sea of Galilee

Trees and animals: *Trees*—ash, beech, date palm, olive, poplar
Animals—antelopes, Arabian oryx, badgers, camels, caracals, cobras, crocodiles, dromedaries, ibexes, lions, leopards, onagers, panthers, wild boars, wolves, zebu oxen

EUROPE

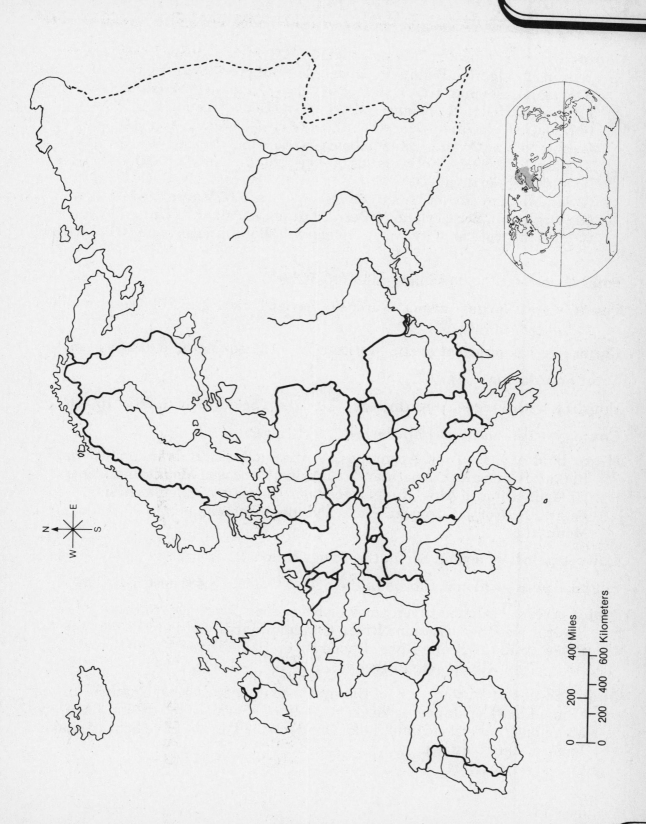

400 Miles

600 Kilometers

200

400

200

400

0

0

200

THE MAP BOOK

FACTS ABOUT
EUROPE

Countries (and ✪capital cities): Albania (✪Tirane), Andorra (✪Andorra), Austria (✪Vienna), Belgium (✪Brussels), Bulgaria (✪Sofia), Czechoslovakia (✪Prague), Denmark (✪Copenhagen), East Germany (✪East Berlin), Finland (✪Helsinki), France (✪Paris), Greece (✪Athens), Hungary (✪Budapest), Iceland (✪Reykjavik), Ireland (✪Dublin), Italy (✪Rome), Liechtenstein (✪Vaduz), Luxembourg (✪Luxembourg), Malta (✪Valletta), Monaco (✪Monaco), Netherlands (✪Amsterdam), Norway (✪Oslo), Poland (✪Warsaw), Portugal (✪Lisbon), Romania (✪Bucharest), San Marino (✪San Marino), Soviet Union (✪Moscow), Spain (✪Madrid), Sweden (✪Stockholm), Switzerland (✪Bern), Turkey (✪Ankara), United Kingdom (✪London), Vatican City, West Germany (✪Bonn), Yugoslavia (✪Belgrade)

Total area: 4,063,000 square miles (10,523,000 sq km)

Country with largest area: European Soviet Union, 2,151,000 square miles (5,571,000 sq km)

Country with smallest area: Vatican City, 0.17 square mile (0.44 sq km)

Total population: 847,679,750

Country with largest population: European Soviet Union, 287,015,000

Country with smallest population: Vatican City, 750

Major land areas: Alps, Apennines, Aquitaine Basin, Balkan Mountains, Balkan Peninsula, Carpathian Mountains, Caucasus Mountains, Central Uplands, Dinaric Alps, Hungarian Basin, Iberian Peninsula, Italian Peninsula, North European Plain, Pyrenees, Scandinavian Peninsula, Ural Mountains

Lowest point: Caspian Sea in the Soviet Union, 92 feet (28 m) below sea level

Highest point: Mount Elbrus in the Soviet Union, 18,481 feet (5,633 m)

Major rivers: Danube River, Dneiper River, Don River, Douro River, Ebro River, Elbe River, Garonne River, Guadalquivir River, Loire River, Oder River, Po River, Rhine River, Rhone River, Seine River, Tagus River, Thames River, Tiber River, Volga River

Major bodies of water: Bay of Biscay, Caspian Sea, English Channel, Lake Como, Lake Constance, Lake Garda, Lake Geneva, Lake Ladoga, Lake Maggione, Lake Neuchatel, Lake Onega, Lake Peipus, Lake Scutari, Lake Vanern, Lake Vattern

THE BRITISH ISLES

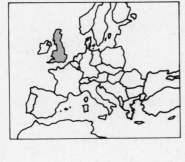

0 50 100 Miles

0 50 100 150 Kilometers

THE MAP BOOK

FACTS ABOUT
THE BRITISH ISLES

Countries (and ☼capital cities):   Ireland (☼Dublin), United Kingdom of Great Britain and Northern Ireland (☼London)

Total area: 121,385 square miles (314,386 sq km)

Lands included in the United Kingdom of Great Britain and Northern Ireland: Great Britain is composed of England (☼London), Scotland (☼Edinburgh), and Wales (☼Cardiff). Northern Ireland comprises six of the nine counties of Ulster (☼Belfast).

Total population: 60,382,000

Country with largest population: United Kingdom of Great Britain and Northern Ireland, 56,648,000

Country with smallest population: Ireland, 3,734,000

Major land areas: Cambrian Mountains, Central Lowlands, Central Plain, Cheviot Hills, Coastal Highlands, Cotswold Hills, Downs, The Fens, Grampian Mountains, Lake District, Midlands (East and West), Mountains of Kerry, Mourne Mountains, Munster Range, Northwest Highlands, Pennine Chain, Southern Uplands, Wicklow Mountains

Lowest point: Along the coasts, sea level

Highest point: Ben Nevis in Scotland, 4,406 feet (1,343 m)

Major rivers: Avon River, Bann River, Barrow River, Blackwater River, Boyne River, Clyde River, Dee River, Exe River, Humber River, Liffey River, Mersey River, Nore River, Ouse River, Severn River, Shannon River, Slaney River, Teifi River, Thames River, Trent River, Tweed River, Tyne River, Wye River

Major bodies of water: Bristol Channel, Cardigan Bay, Donegal Bay, English Channel, Firth of Clyde, Firth of Forth, Galway Bay, Irish Sea, Lake Corrib, Lake Foyle, Lake Neagh, Loch Lomond, Loch Ness, Moray Firth, North Channel, North Sea, St. George's Channel, Solway Firth, Strait of Dover, Tralee Bay, The Wash

Resources, industries, and products: Wheat, oats, barley, potatoes, dairy products, wool, fishing, whiskey, chemicals, coal, oil and gas, iron and steel, mining, engineering, electronics, forestry, motor vehicles, shipbuilding, shipping, banking, insurance, aircraft, textiles, clothing, glass, bone china, porcelain

Unusual facts: The 0° meridian of longitude passes through the Royal Observatory, Greenwich, in Greater London. Big Ben, the bell in the clock tower of the Houses of Parliament, weighs $13\frac{1}{2}$ short tons (12 metric tons).

CENTRAL EUROPE

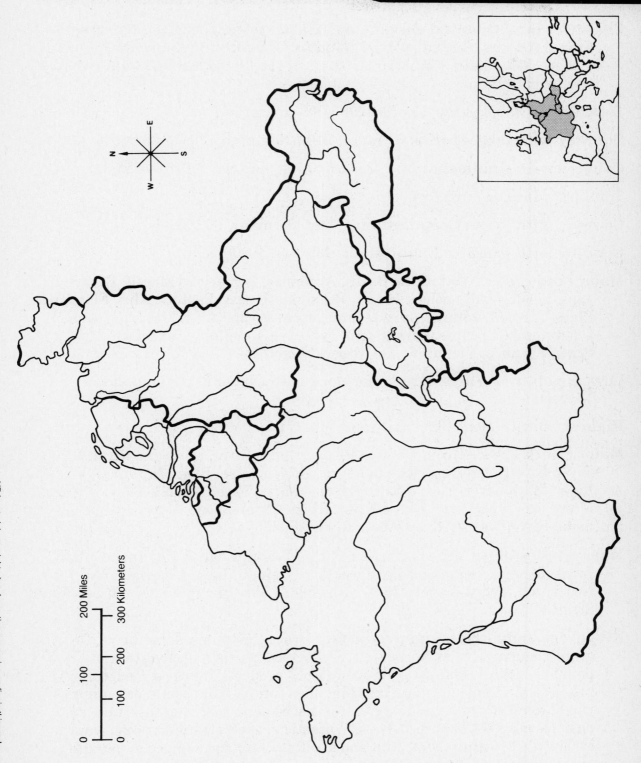

200 Miles

300 Kilometers

FACTS ABOUT
CENTRAL EUROPE

Countries (and ⊙capital cities):   Austria (⊙Vienna), Belgium (⊙Brussels), France (⊙Paris), Liechtenstein (⊙Vaduz), Luxembourg (⊙Luxembourg-Ville), Monaco (⊙Monaco), Netherlands (⊙Amsterdam), Switzerland (⊙Bern), West Germany (⊙Bonn)

Total area: 380,313 square miles (985,003 sq km)

Country with largest area: France, 210,026 square miles (543,965 sq km)

Country with smallest area: Monaco, 0.7 square miles (1.81 sq km)

Total population: 163,564,000

Country with largest population: West Germany, 60,162,000

Country with smallest population: Monaco, 9,000

Major land areas: Aquitaine Basin, Ardennes, Armorican Massif, Bavarian Alps, Bernese Alps, Black Forest, Bohemian Forest, Eastern Alps, Flanders Plain, Harz Mountains, Jura Mountains, Maritime Alps, Massif Central, Odenwald Mountains, Paris Basin, Pyrenees Mountains, Rhaetian Alps, Saxon Uplands, Vienna Basin, Vosges Mountains

Lowest point: An area of reclaimed land northeast of Rotterdam in the Netherlands, 22 feet (7 m) below sea level

Highest point: Mont Blanc in France, 15,771 feet (4,807 m)

Major rivers: Aare River, Danube River, Dender River, Dordogne River, Elbe River, Ems River, Enns River, Garonne River, IJssel River, Inn River, Loire River, Main River, Marne River, Meuse (Maas) River, Moselle (Mosel) River, Mur River, Oise River, Rhine River, Rhône River, Saône River, Schelde River, Seine River, Vechte River, Weser River

Major bodies of water: Baltic Sea, Bay of Biscay, English Channel, Gulf of Lions, IJsselmeer, Lake Constance, Lake Geneva, Lake Lucerne, Lake Neuchâtel, Mediterranean Sea, Neusiedler Lake, North Sea, North Sea Canal, Strait of Dover, Waddenzee

Resources, industries, and products: Grains, potatoes, sugar beets, flax, grapes, orchard fruits, vegetables, flowers, bulbs, fishing, livestock, dairy products, timber, leather, beer, wine, wood products, textiles, foodstuffs, machinery, chemicals, glass making, oil refining, transportation equipment, paper, soap, perfume, building materials, cement, precision instruments, pharmaceuticals, ceramics, tires, synthetic rubber, plastics, watches and clocks, optical equipment, iron and steel, mining, iron ore, coal, bauxite, potash, uranium, slate

EASTERN EUROPE

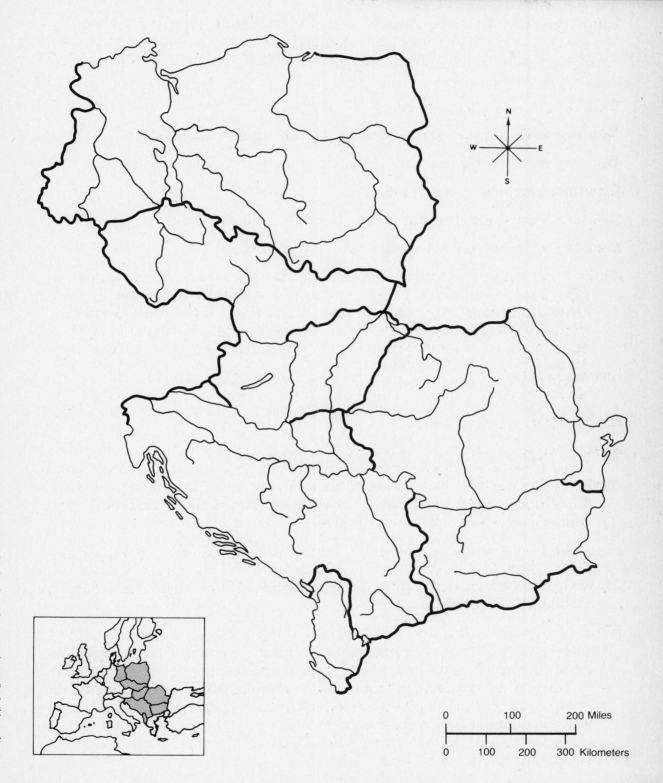

N
W   E
S

0   100   200 Miles

0   100   200   300 Kilometers

FACTS ABOUT
EASTERN EUROPE

Countries (and ✪capital cities):   Albania (✪Tirane), Bulgaria (✪Sofia), Czechoslovakia (✪Prague), East Germany (✪East Berlin), Hungary (✪Budapest), Poland (✪Warsaw), Romania (✪Bucharest), Yugoslavia (✪Belgrade)

Total area: 492,245 square miles (1,274,912 sq km)

Country with largest area: Poland, 120,727 square miles (312,683 sq km)

Country with smallest area: Albania, 11,100 square miles (28,748 sq km)

Total population: 140,503,000

Country with largest population: Poland, 38,389,000

Country with smallest population: Albania, 3,201,000

Major land areas: Balkan Mountains, Balkan Peninsula, Bohemian Forest, Carpathian Mountains, Danube Delta, Danubian tableland, Dinaric Alps, Great Hungarian Plain (Alfold), Harz Mountains, Julian Alps, Moravian Plains, North Albanian Alps, North European Plain, Northern Mountains, Ore Mountains, Pindus Mountains, Rhodope Mountains, Riesengebirge Mountains, Sudeten Mountains, Tatra Mountains, Thuringian Forest, Transylvanian Alps, Transylvanian Basin

Lowest point: Inland from the Gulf of Gdańsk in Poland, 33 feet (10 m) below sea level

Highest point: Musala in Bulgaria, 9,596 feet (2,925 m)

Major rivers: Bosna River, Danube River, Drava River, Drin River, Drina River, Elbe (Labe) River, Iskur River, Kupa River, Maritsa River, Morava River, Mures River, Neisse River, Oder River, Olt River, Prut River, Saale River, Sava River, Siret River, Somes River, Spree River, Struma River, Tisza River, Vardar River, Vijose River, Vistula River, Vltava River

Major bodies of water: Adriatic Sea, Baltic Sea, Black Sea, Gdańsk Bay, Lake Balaton, Lake Ohrid, Lake Prespa, Lake Scutari, Pomeranian Bay, Strait of Otranto

Resources, industries, and products: Grains, potatoes, cotton, corn, sugar beets, grapes, flax, dairy products, livestock, wine, lumber, paper, cement, fertilizers, vehicles, electronics, iron and steel, textiles, clothing, shoes, china, beer, chemicals, ships, pharmaceuticals, coal, oil and gas, chrome, copper, iron, zinc, lead, manganese, silver, potash, bauxite

GREECE AND CYPRUS

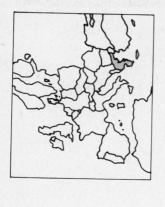

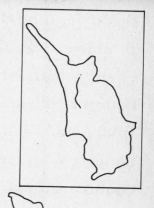

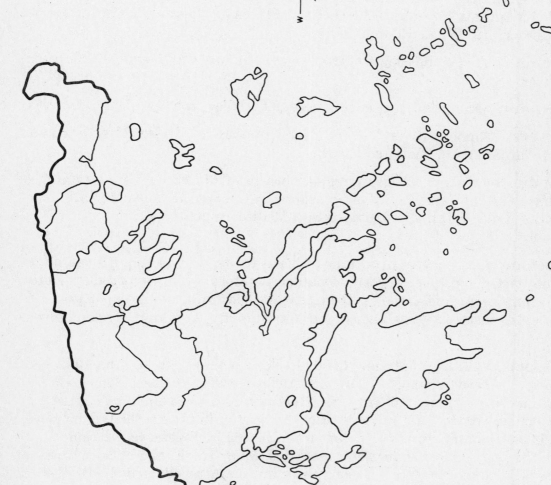

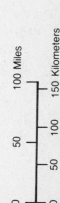

100 Miles

150 Kilometers

FACTS ABOUT
GREECE AND CYPRUS

Countries (and ✪capital cities):   Cyprus (✪Nicosia), Greece (✪Athens)

Total area: 54,521 square miles (141,208 sq km)

Country with largest area: Greece, 50,949 square miles (131,957 sq km)

Country with smallest area: Cyprus, 3,572 square miles (9,251 sq km)

Total population: 10,744,000

Country with largest population: Greece, 10,048,000

Country with smallest population: Cyprus, 696,000

Major land areas: Aegean Islands, Central Plains, Ionian Islands, Larisa Plains, Olympus Mountains, Peloponnesian lowlands, Pentadaktylos Range, Pindus Mountains, Plains of Macedonia, Plains of Thessaly, Plains of Thrace, Salonika Plain, White Plateaus

Lowest point: Along the coasts of the Aegean, Ionian, and Mediterranean seas, sea level

Highest point: Mount Olympus in Greece, 9,570 feet (2,917 m)

Major rivers: Alpheus River, Pedias River, Pinios River, Mesta River, Struma River, Vardar River, Vistritsa River

Major bodies of water: Aegean Sea, Ambracian Gulf, Famagusta Bay, Gulf of Corinth, Gulf of Patras, Gulf of Salonika, Ionian Sea, Lake Kastoria, Lake Koronia, Lake Trikhonis, Larnaca Bay, Mediterranean Sea, Mirtoon Sea, Saronic Gulf, Sea of Crete

Resources, industries, and products: Citrus fruits, raisins, figs, grapes, olives, wheat, barley, sugar beets, corn, tomatoes, potatoes, wine, food products, dairy products, sheep, goats, wool, cotton, textiles, clothing, shoes, paper products, chemicals, plastics, metals, cement, oil, uranium, gypsum, iron, copper, lignite, bauxite, tourism

Unusual facts: Of the more than 2,000 Greek Isles, only 169 are inhabited. Among them are Crete, Corfu, Rhodes, Mykonos, Delos, Lesbos, Samos, Chios, Milos, and Euboea. Most of Greece's rivers dry up in the summer, because three-fourths of the total rainfall occurs in winter. In Greece there is no place that is more than 85 miles (137 km) from the sea. European civilization began in Greece more than 2,000 years ago. Many ruins from ancient times may still be seen in Greece. Among these are the Acropolis and the Parthenon.

THE IBERIAN PENINSULA

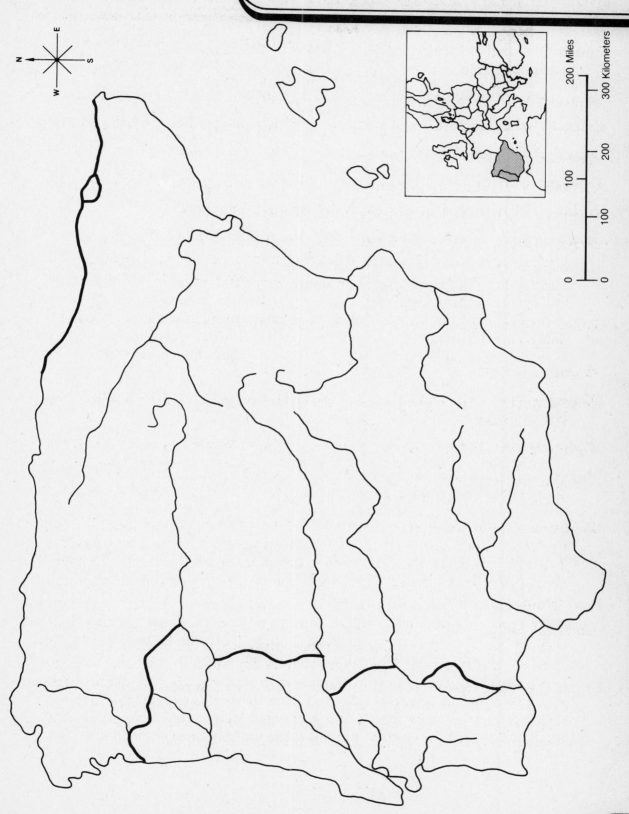

200 Miles

300 Kilometers

200

100

100

0

0

FACTS ABOUT
THE IBERIAN PENINSULA

Countries (and ✪capital cities): Andorra (✪Andorra), Portugal (✪Lisbon), Spain (✪Madrid)

Total area: 228,626 square miles (597,321 sq km)

Country with largest area: Spain, 194,897 square miles (504,782 sq km)

Country with smallest area: Andorra, 180 square miles (467 sq km)

Total population: 50,080,000

Country with largest population: Spain, 39,784,000

Country with smallest population: Andorra, 56,000

Major land areas: Andalusian Basin, Balearic Islands, Beira Litoral, Cantabrian Mountains, Catalan Mountains, Coastal plain, Ebro Basin, Iberian Mountains, Marshes of Aveiro, Mediterranean coastal belt, Meseta, Meseta Central, Montes de Toledo, Northern coastal belt, Penibética Mountains, Plains of Alentejo, Pyrenees Mountains, Serra de Estrela, Serra do Monchique, Sierra de Guadarrama, Sierra Morena, Sierra Nevada, Sintra Hills

Lowest point: Along the coasts of the Atlantic Ocean and the Mediterranean Sea, sea level

Highest point: Mulhacén in Spain, 11,411 feet (3,478 m)

Major rivers: Duero (Douro) River, Ebro River, Guadalquivir River, Guadiana River, Genil River, Jalón River, Júcar River, Miño (Minho) River, Mondego River, Sado River, Segura River, Sorraia River, Tagus (Tejo) River, Tamega River, Zezere River

Major bodies of water: Balearic Sea, Bay of Biscay, Bay of Setúbal, Gulf of Cádiz, Gulf of Valencia, Mediterranean Sea, Strait of Gibraltar

Resources, industries, and products: Potatoes, citrus fruits, grapes, olives, sugar beets, wheat, barley, maize, tomatoes, tobacco, livestock, fish, leather, cork, paper products, wood products, textiles, clothing, footwear, iron, lead, motorcycles, chemicals, ceramics, glass, wine, tourism

Unusual facts: Spain is the third largest country in Europe and the second-highest, after Switzerland. One half of the world's supply of cork comes from Portugal. Andorra is semi-independent under France and Spain. Children may choose to attend either a French or Spanish school.

THE ITALIAN PENINSULA/MALTA

| 0 | | 100 | | 200 Miles |
| 0 | 100 | 200 | 300 Kilometers |

N
W   E
S

FACTS ABOUT THE
ITALIAN PENINSULA/MALTA

Countries (and ✪capital cities): Italy, (✪Rome), Malta (✪Valletta), San Marino (✪San Marino), Vatican City

Total area: 116,470 square miles (301,655 sq km)

Country with largest area: Italy, 116,324 square miles (301,278 sq km)

Country with smallest area: Vatican City, 0.17 square miles (0.44 sq km)

Total population: 57,820,750

Country with largest population: Italy, 57,439,000

Country with smallest population: Vatican City, 750

Major land areas: Apennines, Campagna, Cottian Alps, Dolomites, Graian Alps, Ligurian Alps, Madonie Mountains, Maritime Alps, Mount Titano, Pennines, Plain of Catania, Plain of Foggia, Plain of Lombardy, Po River Valley, the Tirol (Tyrol), Sardinia, Sicily

Lowest point: Along the Mediterranean coast, sea level

Highest points: On the Italian side of Mont Blanc, 15,521 feet (4,731 m); Monte Rosa in Italy, 15,203 feet (4,634 m)

Major rivers: Adige River, Arno River, Piave River, Po River, Tiber River, Ticino River, Tirso River

Major bodies of water: Adriatic Sea, Comino Channels, Gulf of Genoa, Gulf of Naples, Gulf of Salerno, Gulf of Taranto, Gulf of Venice, Ionian Sea, Lake Bolsena, Lake Como, Lake Garda, Lake Maggiore, Lake Trasimene, Ligurian Sea, Malta Channel, Mediterranean Sea, Porto Torres, St. Paul's Bay, Strait of Bonifacio, Strait of Messina, Strait of Otranto, Strait of Sicily, Tyrrhenian Sea, Valletta Harbors

Resources, industries, and products: Wheat, rice, potatoes, onions, olives, grapes, citrus fruits, peaches, tomatoes, livestock, leather goods, woolen goods, ceramics, machinery, automobiles, iron and steel, chemicals, food processing, candy, textiles, shoes and clothing, shipbuilding, paper, cement, mercury, potash, marble, coal, zinc, lead, copper

Unusual facts: Mt. Etna, an active volcano, is located on Sicily. Sicily is the largest island in the Mediterranean Sea. Vatican City is the smallest independent state in the world. The city of Venice has canals instead of streets; its people use boats in place of cars and buses.

SCANDINAVIA

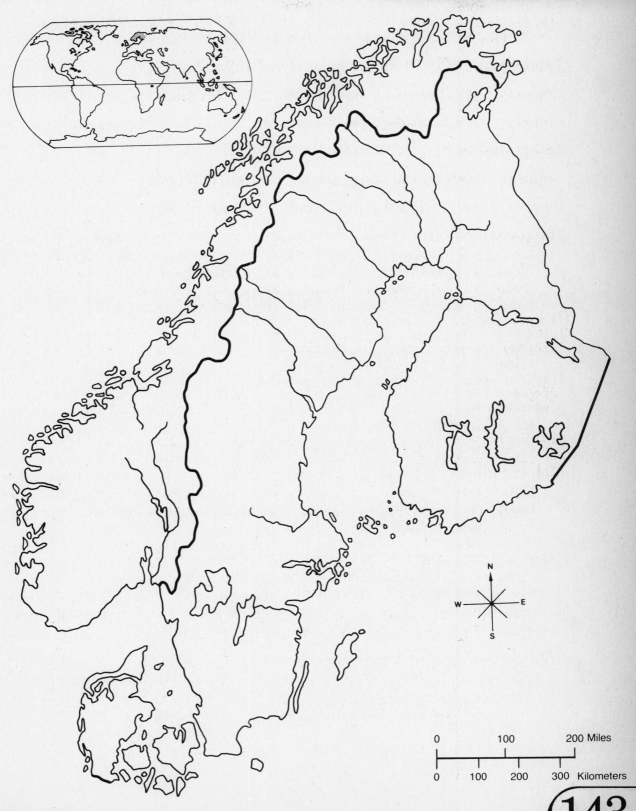

N
W E
S

| 0 | 100 | 200 Miles |

| 0 | 100 | 200 | 300 | Kilometers |

THE MAP BOOK

FACTS ABOUT
SCANDINAVIA

Countries (and ✪capital cities):   Denmark (✪Copenhagen), Finland (✪Helsinki), Norway (✪Oslo), Sweden (✪Stockholm)

Total area: 445,473 square miles (1,253,769 sq km)

Country with largest area: Sweden, 173,229 square miles (448,661 sq km)

Country with smallest area: Denmark, 16,633 square miles (43,080 sq km)

Total population: 22,639,000

Country with largest population: Sweden, 8,371,000

Country with smallest population: Norway, 4,204,000

Major land areas: Baltic Shield, Central Swedish Depression, Coastal plains, Dovrefjell, Finnmark Plateau, Jostedalsbreen Plateau, Jotunheimen Mountains, Jutland Peninsula, Kjolen Mountains, Lake Plateau, Lapland lowland, Rondane massif, Salpaus Ridge, Skane lowlands, Smaland upland, Southern Swedish Highlands, Suomen Ridge, Uppsala Plain

Lowest point: Along the coasts of the Atlantic Ocean, Baltic Sea, Gulf of Bothnia, North Sea, and the Skagerrak, sea level

Highest point: The Glittertind in Norway, 8,110 feet (2,472 m)

Major rivers: Angerman River, Dal River, Glama River, Gota River, Gudena River, Kemi River, Kokemaki River, Lagen River, Lule River, Muonio River, Orkla River, Oulu River, Ounas River, Tornio River, Ume River

Major bodies of water: Arctic Ocean, Baltic Sea, Barents Sea, Gota Canal, Gulf of Bothnia, Gulf of Finland, Imatra Rapids, Kattegat, Lake Hjalmaren, Lake Inari, Lake Malaren, Lake Mjosa, Lake Nasi, Lake Oulu, Lake Paijanne, Lake Pielinen, Lake Saimaa, Lake Vanern, Lake Vattern, North Sea, Norwegian Sea, Oresund, Oslo Fjord, Skagerrak, Sogne Fjord, Trondheims Fjord, Vest Fjord

Resources, industries, and products: Shipbuilding, paper, steel, autos, machinery, textiles, furniture, electronics, chemicals, food processing, oil and gas, timber, dairy products, grains, potatoes, fruits, fish

Unusual facts: In Denmark, there is no place that is more than 45 miles (72 km) from the shore. Denmark has 406 islands, including Greenland, the largest in the world. One third of Norway lies above the Arctic Circle, and it is the northernmost land in Europe. Parts of Sweden and Norway lie within a region called the *Land of the Midnight Sun.* In this region the sun shines 24 hours a day during parts of the summer.

THE SOVIET UNION

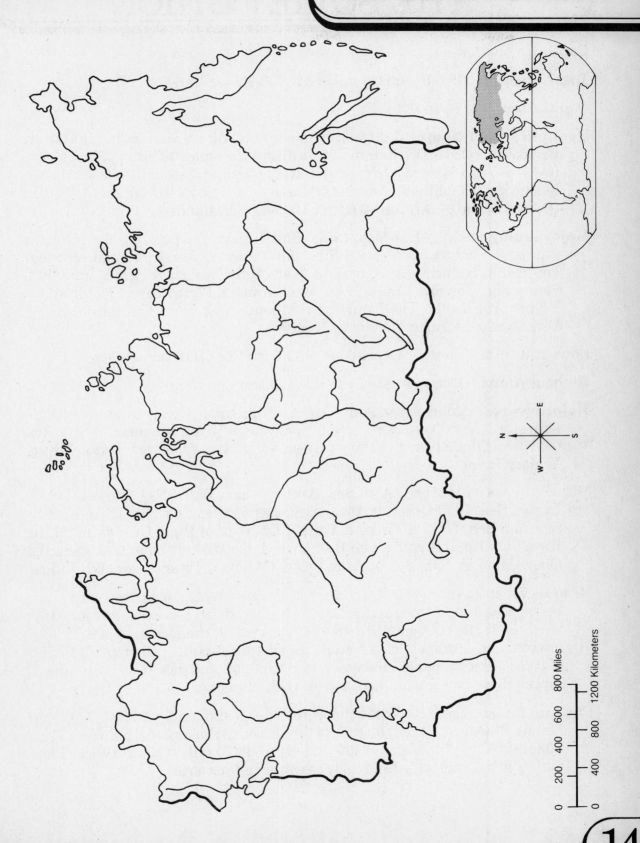

N E
 ✳
W S

800 Miles

1200 Kilometers

200 400 600 800

400 800

0

0

FACTS ABOUT
THE SOVIET UNION

Capital: Moscow

Total area: 8,649,540 square miles (22,402,200 sq km)

Population: 287,015,000

Republics (and ✪capital cities): Armenia (✪Yerevan), Azerbaijan (✪Baku), Belorussia (✪Minsk), Estonia (✪Tallinn), Georgia (✪Tbilisi), Kazakh (✪Alma-Ata), Kirgiz (✪Frunze), Latvia (✪Riga), Lithuania (✪Vilnius), Moldavia (✪Kishinev), Russia (✪Moscow), Tadzhik (✪Dushanbe), Turkmen (✪Ashkhabad), Ukraine (✪Kiev), Uzbek (✪Tashkent)

Major land areas: Altai Mountains, Baltic Plain, Carpathian Mountains, Caucasus Mountains, Central Siberian Plateau, Chersky Range, Crimean Peninsula, Kamchatka Peninsula, Kara-Kum Desert, Kirgiz Steppe, Kola Peninsula, Kolyma Range, Northern European Plain, Sayan Mountains, Taymyr Peninsula, The Pamirs, Ural Mountains, West Siberian Plain, Verkhoyansk Range, Yablonovy Range

Lowest point: Karagie Depression, 433 feet (132 m) below sea level

Highest point: Communism Peak, 24,590 feet (7,495 m)

Major rivers: Aldan River, Amu Darya River, Amur River, Dnieper River, Dniester River, Don River, Irtysh River, Lena River, Northern Dvina River, Ob River, Oka River, Syr Darya River, Volga River, Western Dvina River, Yenisey River

Major bodies of water: Aral Sea, Arctic Ocean, Baltic Sea, Barents Sea, Bering Sea, Bering Strait, Black Sea, Caspian Sea, Chukchi Sea, East Siberian Sea, Gulf of Finland, Gulf of Ob, Gulf of Riga, Gulf of Sakhalin, Kara Sea, Kuril Strait, Lake Balkhash, Lake Baikal, Lake Ladoga, Lake Onega, Laptev Sea, Sea of Azov, Sea of Okhotsk, Tatar Strait, White Sea

Resources, industries, and products: Wheat, barley, oats, rye, corn, sugar beets, potatoes, cotton, hemp, fish, livestock, dairy products, forestry, turbines, machine tools, heavy machinery, iron and steel, chemicals, appliances, locomotives, automobiles, tractors, excavators, fertilizers, artificial fibers, textiles, cement, paper, processed food, coal, oil and gas, iron, manganese, nickel, mercury, potash, salt, silver, gold, diamonds

Unusual facts: Lake Baikal is the world's deepest lake, 5,315 feet (1,620 m). Mount Elbrus at 18,510 feet (5,641 m) is the highest peak in Europe. The Caspian Sea is 746 miles (1200 m) long and 270 miles (434 m) wide. This makes it the largest inland body of water in the world.

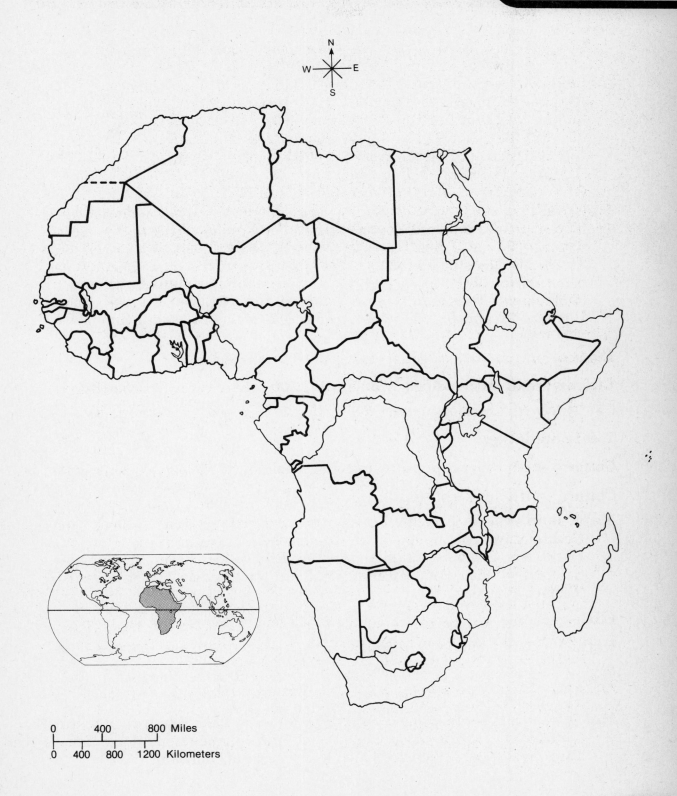

0   400   800 Miles

0   400   800   1200 Kilometers

FACTS ABOUT
AFRICA

Countries (and ✪capital cities):   Algeria (✪Algiers), Angola (✪Luanda), Benin (✪Porto-Novo), Botswana (✪Gaborone), Burkina Faso (✪Ouagadougou), Burundi (✪Bujumbura), Cameroon (✪Yaounde), Cape Verde (✪Praia), Central African Republic (✪Bangui), Chad (✪Ndjamena), Comoros (✪Moroni), Congo (✪Brazzaville), Djibouti (✪Djibouti), Egypt (✪Cairo), Equatorial Guinea (✪Malabo), Ethiopia (✪Addis Ababa), Gabon (✪Libreville), Gambia (✪Banjul), Ghana (✪Accra), Guinea (✪Conakry), Guinea-Bissau (✪Bissau), Ivory Coast (✪Abidjan), Kenya (✪Nairobi), Lesotho (✪Maseru), Liberia (✪Monrovia), Libya (✪Tripoli), Madagascar (✪Antananarivo), Malawi (✪Lilongwe), Mali (✪Bamako), Mauritania (✪Nouakchott), Mauritius (✪Port Louis), Morocco (✪Rabat), Mozambique (✪Maputo), Namibia (✪Windhoek), Niger (✪Niamey), Nigeria (✪Lagos), Rwanda (✪Kigali), São Tome and Principe (✪São Tome), Senegal (✪Dakar), Seychelles (✪Victoria), Sierra Leone (✪Freetown), Somalia (✪Mogadiscio), South Africa (✪Cape Town, Pretoria), Sudan (✪Khartoum), Swaziland (✪Mbabane), Tanzania (✪Dar es Salaam), Togo (✪Lome), Tunisia (✪Tunis), Uganda (✪Kampala), Zaire (✪Kinshasa), Zambia (✪Lusaka), Zimbabwe (✪Harare)

Total area: 11,707,000 square miles (30,320,000 sq km)

Country with largest area: Sudan, 967,500 square miles (2,505,813 sq km)

Country with smallest area: Seychelles, 175 square miles (453 sq km)

Total population: 634,224,900

Country with largest population: Nigeria, 115,152,000

Country with smallest population: Seychelles, 70,000

Major land areas: Ahaggar Plateau, Atlas Mountains, Cape of Good Hope, Coastal Lowlands, Congo Basin, Drakensberg Mountains, Eastern Highlands, Ethiopian Highlands, Great Rift Valley, Ruwenzori Range, Saharan Plateau, Somali Peninsula, Southern Plateau, Tibesti Massif, Western Plateau

Lowest point: Lake Assal in Djibouti, 512 feet (155 m) below sea level

Highest point: Mount Kilimanjaro in Tanzania, 19,340 feet (5,895 m)

Major rivers: Limpopo River, Niger River, Nile River, Orange River, Senegal River, Ubangi River, Vaal River, Zaire (Congo) River, Zambezi River

Major bodies of water: Lake Albert, Lake Chad, Lake Edward, Lake Kariba, Lake Nasser (artificial), Lake Malawi (Nyasa), Lake Rudolf, Lake Tana, Lake Tanganyika, Lake Victoria, Lake Volta, Strait of Gibraltar

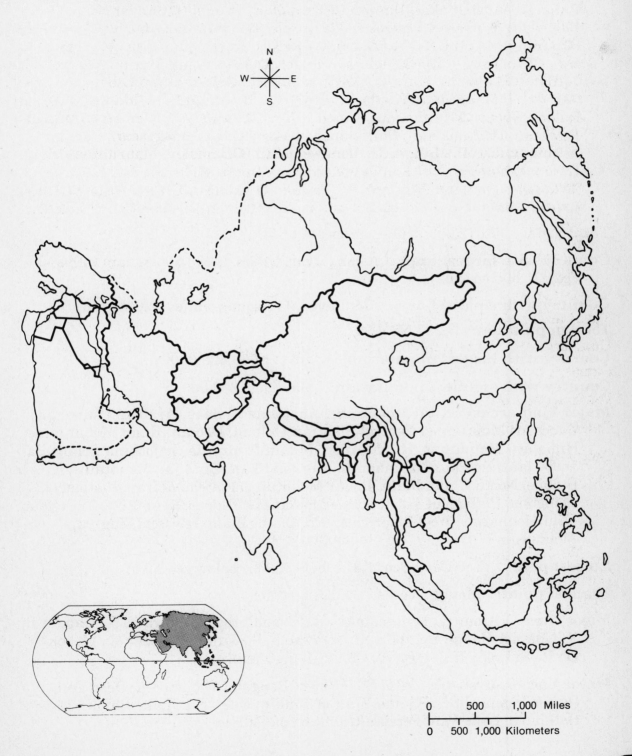

N
W—E
S

0   500   1,000 Miles
0   500 1,000 Kilometers

FACTS ABOUT
ASIA

Countries (and ✪capital cities):   Afghanistan (✪Kabul), Bahrain (✪Manama), Bangladesh (✪Dhaka), Bhutan (✪Thimphu), Brunei (✪Bandar Seri Begawan), Burma (✪Rangoon), Cambodia (✪Phnom Penh), China (✪Beijing), Cyprus (✪Nicosia), India (✪New Delhi), Indonesia (✪Jakarta), Iran (✪Tehran), Iraq (✪Baghdad), Israel (✪Jerusalem), Japan (✪Tokyo), Jordan (✪Amman), Kuwait (✪Kuwait), Laos (✪Vientiane), Lebanon (✪Beirut), Malaysia (✪Kuala Lumpur), Maldives (✪Male), Mongolia (✪Ulan Bator), Nepal (✪Katmandu), North Korea (✪Pyongyang), Oman (✪Muscat), Pakistan (✪Islamabad), Philippines (✪Manila), Qatar (✪Doha), Saudi Arabia (✪Riyadh), Singapore (✪Singapore), South Korea (✪Seoul), Soviet Union (✪Moscow), Sri Lanka (✪Colombo), Syria (✪Damascus), Taiwan (✪Taipei), Thailand (✪Bangkok), Turkey (✪Ankara), United Arab Emirates (✪Abu Dhabi), Vietnam (✪Hanoi), Yemen (✪Sana), Yemen (P.D.R.) (✪Aden)

Total area: 17,012,000 square miles (44,062,000 sq km)

Country with largest area: Asian Soviet Union, 6,498,500 square miles (16,831,000 sq km)

Country with smallest area: Maldives, 115 square miles (298 sq km)

Total population: 3,297,553,000

Country with largest population: China, 1,069,628,000

Country with smallest population: Maldives, 202,000

Major land areas: Altai Mountains, Anatolian Plateau, Arabian Peninsula, Caucasus Mountains, Central Siberian Upland, Deccan, Elburz Mountains, Himalaya Mountains, Hindu Kush, Indian Peninsula, Indochina Peninsula, Indo-Gangetic Plain, Karakoram, Kunlun Shan, Qin Ling Mountains, Kirgiz Steppe, North China Plain, Pamir Mountains, Plateau of Iran, Plateau of Mongolia, Plateau of Tibet, Pontic Mountains, Taurus Mountains, Tian Shan, Ural Mountains, West Siberian Plain, Chang Jiang Lowland, Zagros Mountains

Lowest point: The Dead Sea, 1,312 feet (399 m) below sea level

Highest point: Mount Everest, 29,028 feet (8,848 m)

Major rivers: Amur R., Brahmaputra R., Chao Phraya, Euphrates R., Ganges R., Xi Chiang, Huang He, Indus R., Irrawaddy R., Jordan R., Lena R., Mekong R., Ob R., Salween R., Tigris R., Chang Jiang, Yenisey R.

Major bodies of water: Aral Sea, Bay of Bengal, Caspian Sea, Dead Sea, Gulf of Aden, Gulf of Oman, Gulf of Tonkin, Koko Nor, Lake Baikal, Lake Balkhash, Lake Van, Persian Gulf, Sea of Galilee

CENTRAL ASIA

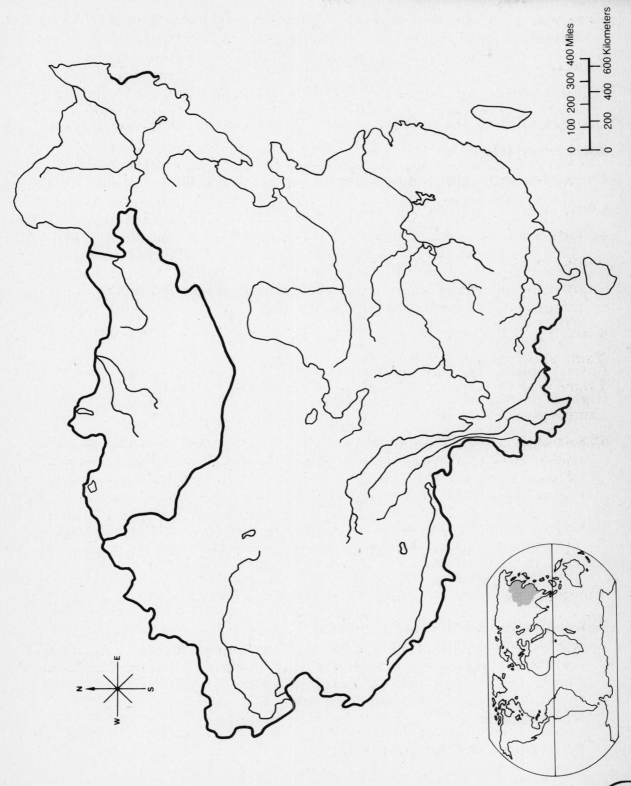

0 100 200 300 400 Miles

0 200 400 600 Kilometers

N E S W

THE MAP BOOK

FACTS ABOUT
CENTRAL ASIA

Countries (and ✪capital cities):   China (✪Beijing), Mongolia (✪Ulan Bator), Taiwan (✪Taipei)

Total area: 3,709,400 square miles (9,607,300 sq km)

Country with largest area: China, 3,695,500 square miles (9,571,300 sq km)

Country with smallest area: Taiwan, 13,900 square miles (36,000 sq km)

Total population: 1,092,004,000

Country with largest population: China, 1,069,628,000

Country with smallest population: Mongolia, 2,093,000

Major land areas: Altai Mountains, Guangzhou Plain, Chang Tang, Qin Ling Mountains, Gobi (Desert), Da Hinggan Ling, Himalaya Mountains, Karakoram Mountains, Kunlun Shan, Liaodong Bandao, Leizhou Bandao, Manchurian Plain, Mongolian Plateau, Nan Shan Range, North China Plain, Shansi Plateau, Shandong Bandao, Sichuan Basin, Taipei Basin, Takla Makan (Desert), Tarim Basin, Qing Zang, Tian Shan Range, Chang Jiang Lowlands, Yunnan Kweichow Plateau

Lowest point: Turfan Depression in China, 505 feet (154 m) below sea level

Highest point: Mount Everest on the Tibet-Nepal border in China, 29,028 feet (8,848 m)

Major rivers: Amur River, Brahmaputra River, Han River, Xi Jiang, Hsiang River, Huang He (Yellow River), Kerulen River, Liao River, Mekong River, Min River, Orhon River, Salween (Nu) River, Selenga River, Songhua Jiang, Tarim He, Wei He, Chang Jiang, Yuan Jiang

Major bodies of water: Amoy Bay, Bashi Channel, East China Sea, Formosa (Taiwan) Strait, Grand Canal, Gulf of Chihli (Po Hai), Gulf of Tonkin, Hainan Strait, Hovsgol Nur, Qingha Hu, Lop Nur Lake, Namu Lake, Poyang Hu, South China Sea, Songhua Jiang Reservoir, Tungting Lake, Uvs Nur, Yellow Sea

Resources, industries, and products: Rice, wheat, sweet potatoes, sorghum, corn, cotton, soybeans, barley, tea, sugarcane, cassava, tropical fruits, vegetables, pigs, food products, petroleum products, paper, iron and steel, machinery, textiles, clothing, fertilizers, chemicals, electronics, pharmaceuticals, instruments, transportation equipment, construction, ceramics, coal, iron ore, oil and gas, tin, tungsten, bauxite

EASTERN ASIA

0   50   100   150 Miles

0   100   200 Kilometers

FACTS ABOUT
EASTERN ASIA

Countries (and ✪capital cities): Japan (✪Tokyo), North Korea (✪Pyongyang), South Korea (✪Seoul)

Total area: 230,648 square miles (597,377 sq km)

Country with largest area: Japan, 145,849 square miles (377,748 sq km)

Country with smallest area: South Korea, 38,259 square miles (99,091 sq km)

Total population: 190,438,000

Country with largest population: Japan, 123,231,000

Country with smallest population: North Korea, 21,964,000

Major land areas: Akaishi Mountains, Changpai Mountains, Han River Plain, Hida (Japan Alps), Hidaka Range, Kanto Plain, Noto Peninsula, Shikoku Range, Sobaek Range

Islands of Japan: Hokkaido, Honshu, Kyushu, Shikoku

Lowest point: Along the coasts, sea level

Highest point: Mount Fuji in Japan, 12,388 feet (3,776 m)

Major rivers: Changjin River, Han River, Imjin River, Ishikari River, Kitikami River, Kum River, Naktong River, Pujon River, Shinano River, Somjin River, Taedong River, Tone River, Tumen River, Yalu River

Major bodies of water: Amakusa Sea, Bungo Strait, Changjin Reservoir, Cheju Strait, East China Sea, Enshu Bay, Inland Sea, Ise Bay, Kanghwa Bay, Korea Bay, Korea Strait, Kumano Bay, La Perouse Strait, Lake Biwa, Osaka Bay, Osumi Strait, Pujon Reservoir, Sea of Japan, Sea of Okhotsk, Suo Sea, Tokyo Bay, Tosa Bay, Toyama Bay, Tsugaro Strait, Wakasa Bay, Uchiura Bay, Yellow Sea

Resources, industries, and products: Rice, grains, corn, soybeans, potatoes, sugar, mulberry bushes (silk), fruits and vegetables, livestock, fishing, processed food, chemicals, fertilizers, machine tools, machinery, shipbuilding, iron and steel, appliances, transportation equipment, electronic equipment, precision and optical instruments, textiles, clothing, cement, ceramics, clay, coal, copper, zinc, lead, manganese, chromite, iron ore, gold, silver

Unusual facts: Lake Kutoharo in Japan is the clearest lake in the world with a transparency of 135 feet (41 m). There are more than 3,000 Korean Islands. Cheju Island which covers about 700 sq. miles (1,800 sq km) is the largest Korean Island.

THE INDIAN SUBCONTINENT

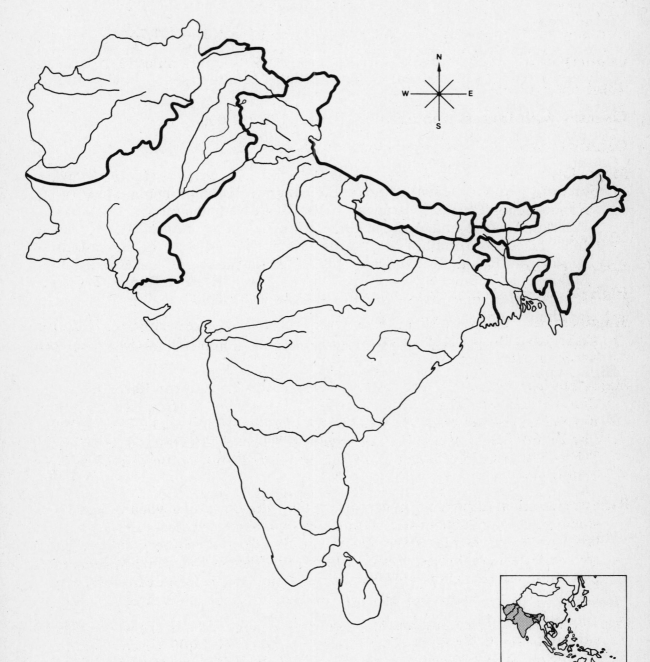

0   200   400 Miles

0   200   400   600 Kilometers

FACTS ABOUT
THE INDIAN SUBCONTINENT

Countries (and ✪ capital cities): Afghanistan (✪Kabul), Bangladesh (✪Dacca), Bhutan (✪Thimphu), India (✪New Delhi), Nepal (✪Kathmandu), Pakistan (✪Islamabad), Sri Lanka (✪Colombo)

Total area: 2,012,438 square miles (5,212,330 sq km)

Country with largest area: India, 1,269,219 square miles (3,287,263 sq km)

Country with smallest area: Bhutan, 17,954 square miles (46,500 sq km)

Total population: 1,110,908,000

Country with largest population: India, 833,422,000

Country with smallest population: Bhutan, 1,538,000

Major land areas: Aravalli Range, Baluchistan Plateau, Central Makran Range, Chagai Hills, Chittagong Hills, Chota Nagpur Plateau, Deccan Plateau, Eastern and Western Ghats, Ganges Delta, Ganges Plain, Great Indian Desert, Himalaya Mountains, Hindu Kush Mountains, Indus Delta, Karakoram Range, Khash Desert, Khasi Hills, Makran Coast Range, Mahabharat Range, Nilgiri Hills, Rann of Kutch, Satpura Range, Siahan Range, Sulaiman Range, Thar Desert, Valley of Nepal, Vindhya Range, Wakhan Valley

Lowest point: Along the coasts of the Arabian Sea and Indian Ocean, sea level

Highest point: Mount Everest between Nepal and Tibet, 29,028 feet (8,848 m)

Major rivers: Amu Darya (Oxus) River, Brahmaputra River, Cauvery River, Chambal River, Chenab River, Gandak River, Ganges River, Ghāghara River, Godavari River, Hari River, Helmand River, Hingol (Nal) River, Indus River, Kabul River, Kali River, Karnali River, Kosi River, Krishna River, Mahanadi River, Mahaweli River, Manas River, Murghab River, Narmada River, Sankosh River, Son River, Sutlej River, Tapti River, Tista River, Yamuna River

Major bodies of water: Arabian Sea, Bay of Bengal, Cape Comorin, Gulf of Cambay, Gulf of Kutch, Gulf of Mannar, Indian Ocean, Laccadive Sea, Lake Gandhi, Palk Bay, Palk Strait

Resources, industries, and products: Rice, jute, tea, peanuts, sugarcane, coconuts, grains, potatoes, corn, cardamom, fruits, cotton, timber, livestock, fishing, chemicals, steel, metal products, fertilizers, machinery, transportation equipment, engineering, cement, textiles, clothing, food processing, paper, oil refining, soap, furniture, handicrafts, bricks, matches, shoes, rubber, stainless steel products, manganese, copper, mica, bauxite, graphite, oil and gas, coal, limestone, iron

SOUTHEAST ASIA

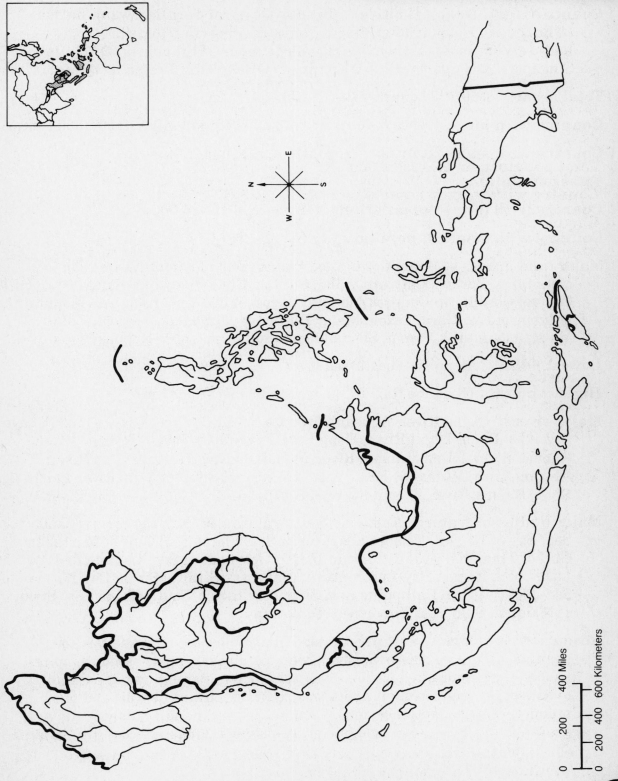

400 Miles

600 Kilometers

200

400

0   200   400

0

FACTS ABOUT SOUTHEAST ASIA

Countries (and ✪capital cities): Brunei (✪Bandar Seri Begawan), Burma (✪Rangoon), Cambodia (✪Phnom Penh), Indonesia (✪Jakarta), Laos (✪Vientiane), Malaysia (✪Kuala Lumpur), Philippines (✪Manila), Singapore (✪Singapore City), Thailand (✪Bangkok), Vietnam (✪Hanoi)

Total area: 1,729,122 square miles (4,478,454 sq km)

Country with largest area: Indonesia, 735,358 square miles (1,904,569 sq km)

Country with smallest area: Singapore, 239 square miles (618 sq km)

Total population: 441,929,000

Country with largest population: Indonesia, 187,726,000

Country with smallest population: Brunei, 267,000

Major land areas: Annam Cordillera, Arakan Yoma Mountains, Barisan Mountains, Borneo, Cagayan Valley, Celebes, Chao Phraya Lowlands, Chin Hills, Central Cordillera, Dangrek Mountains, Indochina Peninsula, Iran Mountains, Isthmus of Kra, Java, Luzon, Malay Peninsula, Mindanao, Mekong Delta, Muller Mountains, Samar, Sierra Madre, Sumatra, Upper Kapuas Mountains

Lowest point: Along the coasts, sea level

Highest point: Hkakabo Razi in Burma, 19,295 feet (5,881 m)

Major rivers: Agno River, Agusan River, Ca River, Cagayan River, Chao Phraya River, Da River, Digul River, Hong River, Irrawaddy River, Kampar River, Kapuas River, Kinabatangan River, Mahakam River, Mamberamo River, Mekong River, Mindanao River, Mun River, Musi River, Pahang River, Pampanga River, Rajang River, Saigon River, Salween River, Sittang River, Ba River

Major bodies of water: Andaman Sea, Arafura Sea, Balabac Strait, Banda Sea, Bay of Bengal, Celebes Sea, Ceram Sea, Flores Sea, Gulf of Martaban, Gulf of Thailand, Gulf of Tonkin, Indian Ocean, Java Sea, Laguna de Bay, Lake Toba, Lamon Bay, Luzon Strait, Makassar Strait, Manila Bay, Mindanao Sea, Molucca Sea, Philippine Sea, Singapore Strait, South China Sea, Strait of Malacca, Sulu Sea, Timor Sea, Tonle Sap

Resources, industries, and products: Pineapples, coconuts, sugarcane, peanuts, corn, rice, cassava, sago, sweet potatoes, pepper, bananas, spices, rubber, cork, copra, tea, coffee, livestock, cotton, fishing, wood, palm oil, textiles, clothing, tires, oil and sugar refining, electronics, oil and gas products, food products, cement, farm machinery, handicrafts, oil and gas, gravel, stone, lead, zinc, gold, silver, gemstones, tungsten, coal, tin, bauxite, chromite

AUSTRALIA, NEW ZEALAND, AND PAPUA NEW GUINEA

N
W E
S

800 Miles
600
400
200
0

1200 Kilometers
800
400
0

THE MAP BOOK

FACTS ABOUT AUSTRALIA, NEW ZEALAND, AND PAPUA NEW GUINEA

Countries (and ✪capital cities): Australia (✪Canberra), New Zealand (✪Wellington), Papua New Guinea (✪Port Moresby)

Total area: 3,248,738 square miles (8,414,197 sq km)

Country with largest area: Australia, 2,966,151 square miles (7,682,300 sq km)

Country with smallest area: New Zealand, 103,883 square miles (269,057 sq km)

Total population: 23,100,000

Country with largest population: Australia, 16,090,000

Country with smallest population: New Zealand, 3,397,000

Major land areas: Arnhem Land, Bismarck Archipelago, Cape York Peninsula, Gibson Desert, Great Artesian Basin, Great Dividing Range, Great Sandy Desert, Great Victoria Desert, Kimberley Plateau, Macdonnell Ranges, Maoke Mountains, Nullarbor Plain, Southern Alps, Swanland

Lowest point: Lake Eyre in Australia, 52 feet (16 m) below sea level

Highest point: Mount Wilhelm in Papua New Guinea, 14,762 feet (4,499 m)

Major rivers: Ashburton River, Clutha River, Darling River, Fitzroy River, Fly River, Lachlan River, Mitchell River, Murray River, Murrumbidgee River, Ramu River, Sepik River, Strickland River, Victoria River, Waikato River

Major bodies of water: Arafura Sea, Bass Strait, Bay of Plenty, Cook Strait, Coral Sea, Foveaux Strait, Great Australian Bight, Gulf of Carpentaria, Gulf of Papua, Hauraki Gulf, Hawke Bay, Indian Ocean, Lake Taupo, Lake Te Anau, Pacific Ocean, Solomon Sea, Tasman Bay, Tasman Sea, Timor Sea, Torres Strait

Resources, industries, and products: Coffee, cocoa, sugarcane, tea, fruit, rice, copra, wheat, barley, oats, vegetables, sheep, cattle, dairy products, wool, food products, paper products, wood, textiles, chemicals, beverages, rubber, plastics, machinery, electronics equipment, mining, iron ore, cement, copper, gold, coal, oil, diamonds, uranium

Unusual facts: The Great Barrier Reef, off the east coast of Queensland, Australia, is the longest coral reef (1,200 miles or 1,900 km) in the world. Southerland Falls tumbles 1,904 feet (580 m) down a mountain in New Zealand, making it the fourth highest waterfall in the world.

THE WESTERN HEMISPHERE

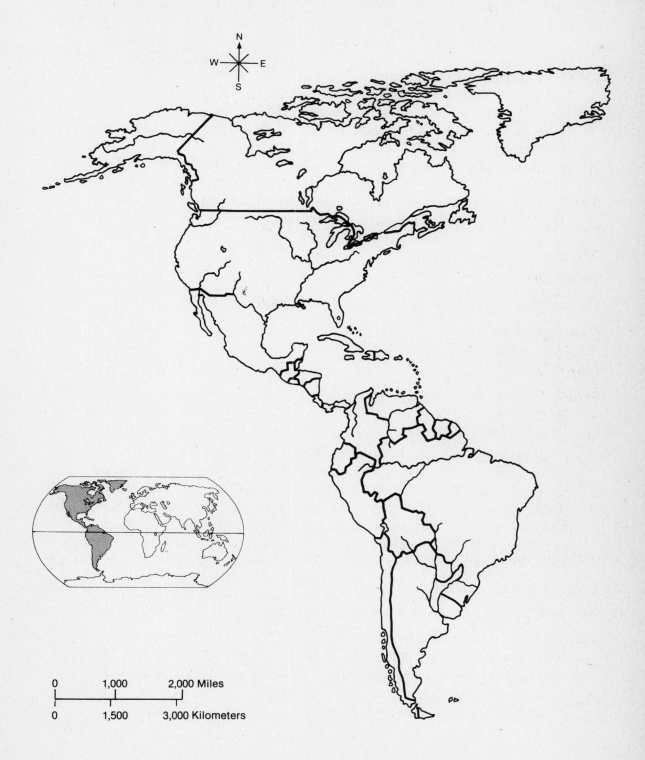

0   1,000   2,000 Miles

0   1,500   3,000 Kilometers

THE MAP BOOK

FACTS ABOUT
THE WESTERN HEMISPHERE

Countries (and ✪capital cities): Antigua and Barbuda (✪St. John's), Argentina (✪Buenos Aires), Bahamas (✪Nassau), Barbados (✪Bridgetown), Belize (✪Belmopan), Bolivia (✪La Paz, Sucre), Brazil (✪Brasilia), Canada (✪Ottawa), Chile (✪Santiago), Colombia (✪Bogota), Costa Rica (✪San Jose), Cuba (✪Havana), Dominica (✪Roseau), Dominican Republic (✪Santo Domingo), Ecuador (✪Quito), El Salvador (✪San Salvador), Federation of St. Christopher and Nevis (✪Basseterre), French Guiana—part of France, Greenland—part of Denmark, Grenada (✪St. George's), Guatemala (✪Guatemala City), Guyana (✪Georgetown), Haiti (✪Port-au-Prince), Honduras (✪Tegucigalpa), Jamaica (✪Kingston), Mexico (✪Mexico City), Nicaragua (✪Managua), Panama (✪Panama City), Paraguay (✪Asuncion), Peru (✪Lima), St. Lucia (✪Castries), St. Vincent and the Grenadines (✪Kingston), Suriname (✪Paramaribo), Trinidad and Tobago (✪Port of Spain), United States (✪Washington, D.C.), Uruguay (✪Montevideo), Venezuela (✪Caracas)

Total area: 16,304,000 square miles (42,277,000 sq km)

Country with largest area: Canada, 3,553,308 square miles (9,203,054 sq km)

Country with smallest area: Grenada, 133 square miles (344 sq km)

Total population: 757,421,438

Country with largest population: United States, 237,480,000

Country with smallest population: Federation of St. Christopher and Nevis, 40,000

Major land areas: *North America*—Alaska Range, Appalachian Mountains, Appalachian Plateau, Basin and Range Region, Brooks Range, Canadian Shield, Cascade Range, Central Valley (California), Coast Ranges, Colorado Plateau, Columbia Plateau, Interior Plains, Mexican Plateau, Piedmont, Rocky Mountains, Sierra Madre Occidental, Sierra Madre Oriental, Sierra Nevada, Yucatán Peninsula *South America*—Amazon Basin, Andes Mountains, Brazilian Highlands, Cape Horn, Central Plains, Guiana Highlands, Isthmus of Panama, Pacific Coastlands, Patagonian Plateau

Lowest point: Death Valley in the U.S., 282 feet (86 m) below sea level

Highest point: Mount Aconcagua in Argentina, 22,831 feet (6,959 m)

Major rivers: Amazon R., Colorado R., Columbia R., Mackenzie R., Madeira R., Mississippi R., Missouri R., Nelson R., Ohio R., Orinoco R., Paraguay R., Parana R., Rio Grande, Rio de la Plata, St. Lawrence R., Uruguay R., Yukon R.

Major bodies of water: Caribbean Sea, Great Bear Lake, Great Salt Lake, Great Slave Lake, Gulf of Mexico, Hudson Bay, Lake Athabasca, Lake Erie, Lake Huron, Lake Maracaibo, Lake Michigan, Lake Nicaragua, Lake Ontario, Lake Superior, Lake Titicaca, Lake Winnipeg

CANADA

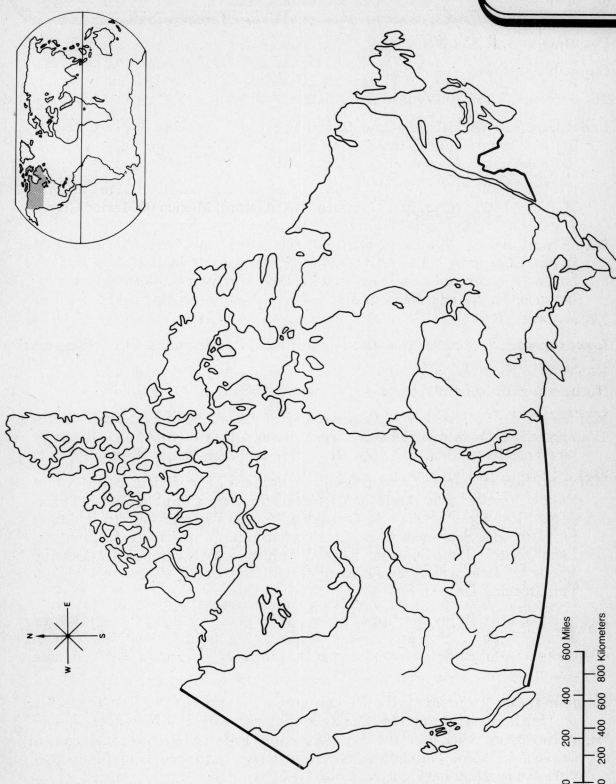

600 Miles

800 Kilometers

FACTS ABOUT
CANADA

Population: 25,334,000

Capital: Ottawa

Total area: 3,553,308 square miles (9,203,054 sq km)

Provinces and Territories (and ✪capital cities):   Alberta (✪Edmonton), British Columbia (✪Victoria), Manitoba (✪Winnipeg), New Brunswick (✪Fredericton), Newfoundland (✪St. John's), Northwest Territories (✪Yellowknife), Nova Scotia (✪Halifax), Ontario (✪Toronto), Prince Edward Island (✪Charlottetown), Québec (✪Québec), Saskatchewan (✪Regina), Yukon Territory (✪Whitehorse)

Major land areas: Appalachian Highlands, Arctic Islands (Baffin, Banks, Devon, Ellesmere, Victoria), Canadian Shield, Coast Mountains, Great Lakes-St. Lawrence Lowlands, Hudson Bay Lowlands, Interior Plains, Labrador Highlands, Newfoundland, Rocky Mountains, Ungava Peninsula, Yukon Plateau

Lowest point: Along the coasts of the Atlantic, Pacific, and Arctic oceans and Hudson Bay, sea level

Highest point: Mount Logan, 19,850 feet (6,050 m)

Major rivers: Albany River, Athabasca River, Churchill River, Columbia River, Fraser River, Mackenzie River, Nelson River, Ottawa River, Peace River, St. Lawrence River, Saskatchewan River, Severn River, Yukon River

Major bodies of water: Arctic Ocean, Athabasca Lake, Baffin Bay, Bay of Fundy, Beaufort Sea, Davis Strait, Fox Basin, Grand Bank, Great Bear Lake, Great Slave Lake, Gulf of St. Lawrence, Hudson Bay, Hudson Strait, James Bay, Labrador Sea, Lake Erie, Lake Huron, Lake Manitoba, Lake Nipigon, Lake Ontario, Lake Superior, Lake Winnipeg, Lake Winnipegosis, Lake of the Woods, St. Lawrence Seaway, Strait of Belle Isle, Strait of Juan de Fuca, Thunder Bay, Ungava Bay

Resources, industries, and products: Transportation equipment, machinery, chemicals, paper, iron and steel, food processing, mining, livestock, fish, oil and gas, lumber, dairy products, wheat, oats, barley, corn, copper, lead, zinc, nickel

Unusual facts: Canada is the second-largest country in the world, but a third of it is almost uninhabited. The Reversing Falls of Saint John may be seen in New Brunswick near the Bay of Fundy. At low tide the water falls toward the sea. At high tide a strong current rushes in from the Bay of Fundy and pushes the water backwards over the falls.

MEXICO/CENTRAL AMERICA

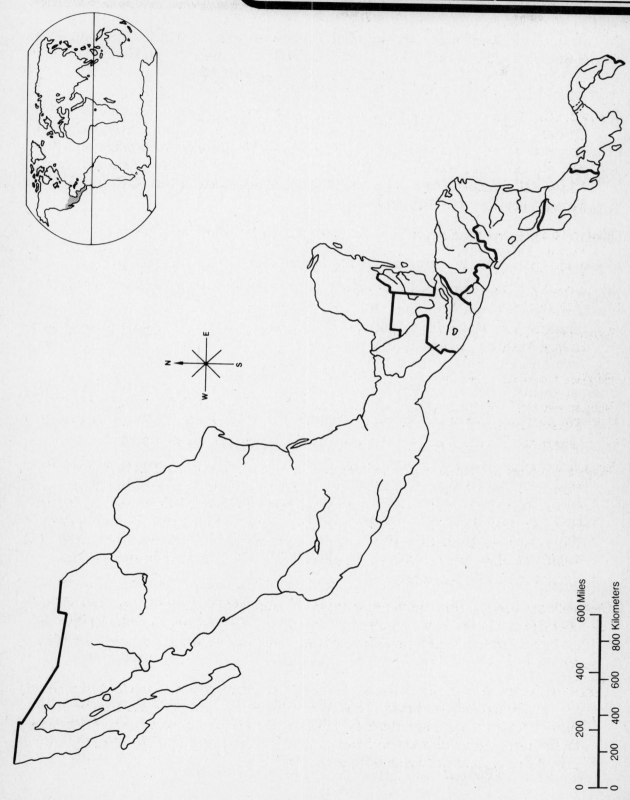

600 Miles

800 Kilometers

400

600

200

400

200

0

0

THE MAP BOOK

FACTS ABOUT
MEXICO/CENTRAL AMERICA

Countries (and ✪capital cities): Belize (✪Belmopan), Costa Rica (✪San Jose), El Salvador (✪San Salvador), Guatemala (✪Guatemala City), Honduras (✪Tegucigalpa), Mexico (✪Mexico City), Nicaragua (✪Managua), Panama (✪Panama City)

Total area: 954,435 square miles (2,471,972 sq km)

Country with largest area: Mexico, 756,066 square miles (1,958,201 sq km)

Country with smallest area: El Salvador, 8,260 square miles (21,393 sq km)

Total population: 117,316,400

Country with largest population: Mexico, 88,087,000

Country with smallest population: Belize, 179,400

Major land areas: Azuero Peninsula, Baja California Peninsula, Caribbean Lowlands, Central Plateau, Gulf Coast, Isthmus of Panama, Isthmus of Tehuantepec, Mosquito (Miskitos) Coast, Pacific Coastal Strip, Sierra Madre (Sierra Madre Occidental, Sierra Madre Oriental, Sierra Madre del Sur), Yucatán Peninsula

Lowest point: Along the Pacific and Caribbean coasts, sea level

Highest point: Pico de Orizaba in Mexico, 18,700 feet (5,700 m)

Major rivers: Aguán River, Belize River, Chepo River, Choluteca River, Chucunaque River, Coco (Segovia) River, Conchos River, Escondido River, Grijalva River, Lempa River, Lerma River, Motagua River, New River, Panuco River, Papaloapan River, Pasión River, Patuca River, Paz River, Polochic River, Río Bravo del Norte (Rio Grande), Rio de las Balsas, Río Grande de Matagalpa, Río Grande de Santiago, Río San Carlos, Río Sibun, San Juan River, Soto la Marina, Tuira River, Ulúa River, Usumacinta River, Yaqui River

Major bodies of water: Amatique Bay, Bay of Campeche, Caratasca Lagoon, Caribbean Sea, Chetumal Bay, Coronado Bay, Gulf of California, Gulf of Chiriquí, Gulf of Fonseca, Gulf of Honduras, Gulf of Mexico, Gulf of Nicoya, Gulf of Panama, Gulf of Tehuantepec, Lake Atitlán, Lake Chapala, Lake Izabal, Lake Managua, Lake Nicaragua, Lake Toronto, Mosquito Gulf, Panama Canal

Resources, industries, and products: Coffee, bananas, sugar, cacao, cotton, rice, citrus fruits, maize, beans, wheat, livestock, leather goods, furniture, wood products, cement, textiles, fertilizers, pharmaceuticals, food processing, clothing, timber, fishing, chemicals, metal products, oil and gas, salt, limestone, bauxite, gold, silver, lead, zinc, tourism

SOUTH AMERICA

| 0 | 200 | 400 | 600 Miles |

| 0 | 400 | 800 Kilometers |

THE MAP BOOK

FACTS ABOUT
SOUTH AMERICA

Countries (and ✪capital cities): Argentina (✪Buenos Aires), Bolivia (✪Sucre — legal and ✪La Paz — de facto), Brazil (✪Brasília), Chile (✪Santiago), Colombia (✪Bogotá), Ecuador (✪Quito), French Guiana (✪Cayenne), Guyana (✪Georgetown), Paraguay (✪Asunción), Peru (✪Lima), Suriname (✪Paramaribo), Uruguay (✪Montevideo), Venezuela (✪Caracas)

Total area: 6,869,570 square miles (17,792,112 sq km)

Country with largest area: Brazil, 3,286,488 square miles (8,511,965 sq km)

Country with smallest area: French Guiana, 34,750 square miles (90,000 sq km)

Total population: 348,472,038

Country with largest population: Brazil, 153,992,000

Country with smallest population: French Guiana, 92,038

Major land areas: Altiplano, Amazon Basin, Andes Mountains, Atacama Desert, Brazilian Highlands, Coastal Plain, Cordillera Central, Cordillera Occidental, Cordillera Oriental, Falkland Islands, Gran Chaco, Guiana Highlands, Llanos, Mato Grosso Plateau, Montaña, Pacific Coastlands, Pampas, Patagonian Plateau, Selvas

Lowest point: Valdés Peninsula in Argentina, 131 feet (40 m) below sea level

Highest point: Mount Aconcagua in Argentina, 22,834 feet (6,960 m)

Major rivers: Amazon River, Apurímac River, Arauca River, Beni River, Bío-bío River, Cauca River, Coppename River, Courantyne River, Esmeraldas River, Guaporé River, Guaviare River, Huallaga River, Madeira River, Madre de Dios River, Magdalena River, Mamoré River, Marañón River, Maroni River, Meta River, Orinoco River, Pará River, Paraguay River, Paraná River, Pilcomayo River, Río Negro, Río de la Plata, São Francisco River, Tocantins River, Ucayali River, Urubamba River, Uruguay River, Xingu River

Major bodies of water: Angel Falls, Atlantic Ocean, Caribbean Sea, Corcovado Gulf, Gulf of Guayaquil, Gulf of San Jorge, Gulf of Venezuela, Lake Maracaibo, Lake Mar Chiquita, Lake Poopó, Lake Titicaca, Patos Lagoon, Penas Gulf, Samborombón Bay, San Matías Gulf, Strait of Magellan

Resources, industries, and products: Coffee, bananas, sugarcane, beef, grains, cotton, wool, fishing, leather, food processing, wood products, timber, textiles, chemicals, plastics, steel, autos, tin, oil and gas, aluminum, bauxite, iron ore, gold, platinum, emeralds

POLITICAL MAP OF THE WORLD

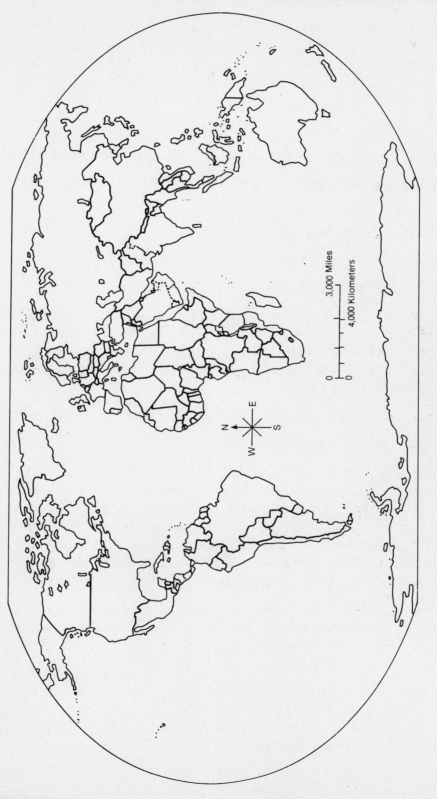

3,000 Miles

4,000 Kilometers

PHYSICAL MAP OF THE WORLD

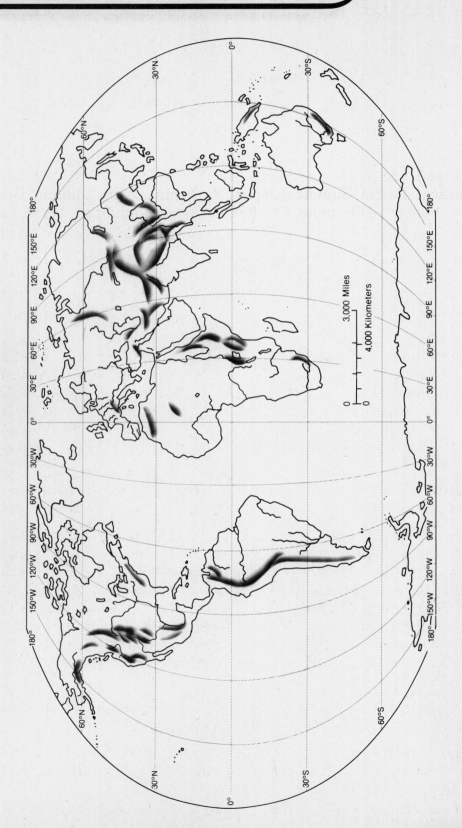

3,000 Miles

4,000 Kilometers

FACTS ABOUT
THE WORLD

Total area: 196,950,000 square miles (510,100,500 sq km)

Total land area: 57,800,000 square miles (149,702,000 sq km)

Total water area: 139,150,000 square miles (360,398,500 sq km)

Continents: Africa, Antarctica, Asia, Australia, Europe, North America, South America

Major islands and island groups (by size): Greenland, New Guinea, Borneo, Madagascar, Baffin, Sumatra, Japan, Philippines, New Zealand, Great Britain, Victoria, Ellesmere, Celebes, Java, Newfoundland, Cuba, Luzon, Iceland, Mindanao, Molucca Islands, Movaya Zemlya, Ireland, Sakhalin

Major bodies of water: Arctic Ocean, Atlantic Ocean, Baltic Sea, Bering Sea, Black Sea, Caribbean Sea, Gulf of Mexico, Hudson Bay, Indian Ocean, Mediterranean Sea, North Sea, Pacific Ocean, Red Sea, Sea of Japan, Sea of Okhotsk, South China Sea

Major mountain ranges: Alaska Range, Alps, Altai Mts., Apennines, Appalachian Mts., Atlas Mts., Balkan Mts., Brooks Range, Carpathian Mts., Cascade Range, Caucasus Mts., Coast Ranges, Dinaric Alps, Drakensberg Mts., Himalaya Mts., Hindu Kush, Karakoram-Kunlun-Nan Shan-Tsinling Shan Mts., Lebanon Mts., Oman Mts., Pamir Mts., Pontic Mts., Pyrenees, Rocky Mts., Ruwenzori Range, Sierra Madre Occidental, Sierra Madre Oriental, Sierra Nevada, Taurus Mts., Tien Shan, Ural Mts., Zagros Mts.

Major deserts: Atacama Desert, Australian Desert, Gobi, Kalahari Desert, Kara Kum, Kyzyl Kum, Libyan Desert, Negev, North American Desert, Rub al Khali, Sahara, Syrian Desert, Takla Makan, Thar Desert

Climate: The regions near the North and South Poles are cold, with long winters and short summers. Yearly precipitation is less than 10 inches (25 cm). The climate is polar near the poles and subarctic near the Arctic and Antarctic Circles. In the tropical lands near the equator, it is hot all year round. Yearly precipitation can be over 60 inches (150 cm). In the Tropic of Cancer and the Tropic of Capricorn, climates are subtropical, semiarid, or arid. Precipitation gets lighter as you move away from the equator. Between the Tropics and the Circles, climates tend to be mild, with warm summers and cool-to-cold winters.

Ten largest countries (by size): Soviet Union, Canada, China, United States, Brazil, Australia, India, Argentina, Sudan, Algeria

Ten largest countries (by population): China, India, Soviet Union, United States, Indonesia, Brazil, Japan, Nigeria, Mexico, West Germany

Continued on page 172.

FACTS ABOUT
THE WORLD

Countries:

Afghanistan
Albania
Algeria
Andorra
Angola
Antigua and
    Barbuda
Argentina
Australia
Austria
Bahamas
Bahrain
Bangladesh
Barbados
Belgium
Belize
Benin
Bhutan
Bolivia
Botswana
Brazil
Brunei
Bulgaria
Burkina Faso
Burma
Burundi
Cambodia
Cameroon
Canada
CapeVerde
Central African
    Republic
Chad
Chile
China
Colombia
Comoros
Congo
Costa Rica
Cuba
Cyprus
Czechoslovakia
Denmark
Djibouti
Dominica
Dominican Republic

East Germany
Ecuador
Egypt
El Salvador
Equatorial Guinea
Ethiopia
Federation of St.
    Christopher and
    Nevis
Fiji
Finland
France
Gabon
Gambia
Ghana
Greece
Grenada
Guatemala
Guinea
Guinea-Bissau
Guyana
Haiti
Honduras
Hungary
Iceland
India
Indonesia
Iran
Iraq
Ireland
Israel
Italy
Ivory Coast
Jamaica
Japan
Jordan
Kenya
Kiribati
Kuwait
Laos
Lebanon
Lesotho
Liberia
Libya
Liechtenstein
Luxembourg

Madagascar
Malawi
Malaysia
Maldives
Mali
Malta
Mauritania
Mauritius
Mexico
Monaco
Mongolia
Morocco
Mozambique
Namibia
Nauru
Nepal
Netherlands
New Zealand
Nicaragua
Niger
Nigeria
North Korea
Norway
Oman
Pakistan
Panama
Papua New Guinea
Paraguay
Peru
Philippines
Poland
Portugal
Quatar
Romania
Rwanda
St. Lucia
St. Vincent and the
    Grenadines
San Marino
São Tome and
    Principe
Saudi Arabia
Senegal
Seychelles
Sierra Leone
Singapore

Solomon Islands
Somalia
South Africa
South Korea
Soviet Union
Spain
Sri Lanka
Sudan
Suriname
Swaziland
Sweden
Switzerland
Syria
Taiwan
Tanzania
Thailand
Togo
Tonga
Trinidad and
    Tobago
Tunisia
Turkey
Tuvalu
Uganda
United Arab
    Emirates
United Kingdom
United States
Uruguay
Vanuata
Vatican City
Venezuela
Vietnam
Western Samoa
West Germany
Yemen (P.D.R.)
Yemen (Sana)
Yugoslavia
Zaire
Zambia
Zimbabwe

MAP OF THE CONTINENTS

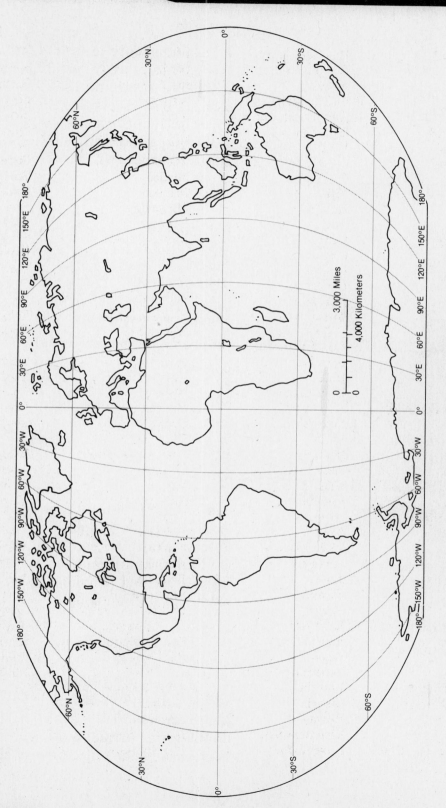

NAME _____

FACTS ABOUT
THE CONTINENTS

AREA

Asia	17,012,000 square miles (44,062,000 sq km)
Africa	11,707,000 square miles (30,320,000 sq km)
North America	9,362,000 square miles (24,247,500 sq km)
South America	6,884,000 square miles (17,830,000 sq km)
Antarctica	5,500,000 square miles (14,425,000 sq km)
Europe	4,063,000 square miles (10,523,000 sq km)
Australia	2,967,700 square miles (7,686,000 sq km)

WHERE PEOPLE LIVE

Asia	3,297,553,000
Europe	847,679,750
North America	757,421,438
Africa	634,224,900
South America	348,472,038
Australia	16,090,000
Antarctica	no permanent population

POPULATION DENSITY (number of people per square mile)

Europe	208
Asia	193
North America	80
Africa	54
South America	50
Australia	5

LARGEST CITY ON EACH CONTINENT

North America	Mexico City (10 million people)
Asia	Seoul (9 million people)
Europe	Moscow (8 million people)
South America	Sao Paulo (7 million people)
Africa	Cairo (6 million people)
Australia	Sydney (3 million people)

COASTLINE LENGTH

North America	74,888 miles (122,521 km)
Asia	58,582 miles (94,280 km)
Europe	30,787 miles (49,506 km)
South America	24,783 miles (39,884 km)
Africa	22,469 miles (36,160 km)
Australia	12,466 miles (20,030 km)
Antarctica	unknown—edge of ice always changing

WESTERN AND EASTERN HEMISPHERES

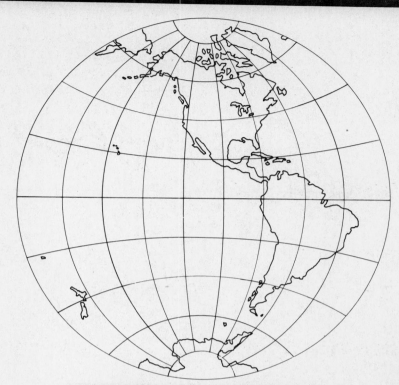

THE WESTERN HEMISPHERE

THE EASTERN HEMISPHERE

THE MAP BOOK

NORTHERN AND SOUTHERN HEMISPHERES

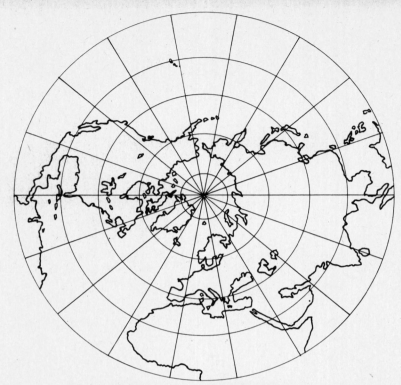

THE NORTHERN HEMISPHERE

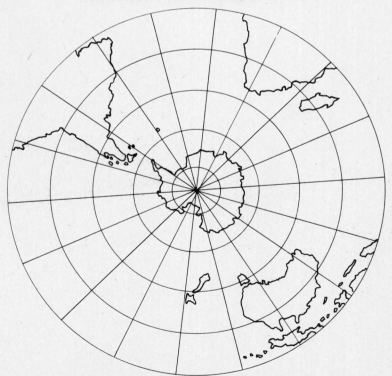

THE SOUTHERN HEMISPHERE

B 1
C 2
D 3
E 4
F 5
G 6
H 7
I 8
J 9

0

THE MAP BOOK